A Photog

SNAKES AND OTHER REPTILES OF THAILAND AND SOUTHEAST ASIA

Merel J. Cox, Peter Paul van Dijk,
Jarujin Nabhitabhata
and Kumthorn Thirakhupt

ASIA BOOKS

Published and distributed in Thailand by
Asia Books Co., Ltd.
5 Sukhumvit Road, Soi 61,
P.O. Box 40, Bangkok 10110, Thailand
Tel. (66-2) 714-0740-2 ext. 221–223
Fax. (66-2) 391-2277, 381-1621

ISBN 1 85368 438 4

Commissioning editor: Jo Hemmings
Edited, designed and cartography by D & N Publishing, Membury Business Park, Lambourn Woodlands, Hungerford, Berkshire

Reproduction by Modern Age Repro House Limited, Hong Kong
Printed and bound in Malaysia by Times Offset (M) Sdn Bhd

10 9 8 7 6 5 4 3 2 1

Front cover photograph: White-lipped Pit-viper (Anita Malhotra)
Back cover photograph: Mangrove Snake (Peter Paul van Dijk)
Title page photograph: Big-headed Turtle (Peter Paul van Dijk)

All photographs by Peter Paul van Dijk unless stated otherwise.

Acknowledgements
We are most grateful to our many colleagues and friends who provided us with slides for inclusion in this book: Henrik Bringsøe, Ashok Captain, Tanya Chan-ard, Lawan Chanhome, Raynoo Homhual Cox, Jennifer Daltry, Indraneil Das, Wolfgang Denzer, Wolfgang Grossmann, Andreas Gümprecht, Piboon Jintakune, Lim Boo Liat, Anita Malhotra, Ulrich Manthey, Peter Mudde, Musa Mumen, Suthigit Patramangorn, Pratheep Rojanadilok, Klaus-Dieter Schulz, Mark O'Shea, Robert B. Stuebing, Roger S. Thorpe, Gernot Vogel, Harold K. Voris, Don Wells, Romulus Whitaker and Wolfgang Wüster. We also thank Pongsakorn Arnamica, Lawan Chanhome, Kittipong Jarutanin, Wachira Kitimasak and Panya Youngprapakorn for access to animals for photography.

We wish to thank our host institutions and research sponsors who made it possible for us to observe animals in the wild and analyse the information collected: Thailand Institute of Scientific and Technological Research at the National Research Council, Bangkok; the Queen Saovabha Memorial Institute of the Thai Red Cross Society; Chulalongkorn University, Bangkok; the National University of Ireland at Galway; the Turtle Recovery Program, New York; the Wildlife Conservation Society, New York; the Seub Nakhasathien Foundation, Bangkok; the International Union for the Conservation of Nature and Natural Resources (IUCN); the Nature Conservation Bureau of the Environment Agency of Japan; and the National Science Museum, Bangkok. We also thank the staff of the Technical, Wildlife Conservation and National Parks Divisions of the Royal Forest Department of Thailand for their practical assistance and other courtesies, as well as our many field companions and correspondents. Last and best, we give our heartfelt thanks to our families for their support, patience, tolerance and understanding for our tendency to let reptiles take priority over all else.

Contents

Introduction

The study of the herpetofauna of Southeast Asia has a relatively short history, but it has received the full attention of some of the best researchers. Consequently, much is already known about the species diversity of the regional herpetofauna, although we are still far from acquiring complete knowledge. In recent decades, interest has proceeded beyond species identification and the description of new species to include ecological research on habitats and the impact of human activities on natural and other ecosystems. At the same time, local and international tourism has discovered the forests, beaches and other unspoilt habitats of Southeast Asia as an attractive destination.

These developments clearly indicated the need for a guide to identify at least the common, conspicuous reptile species and to provide some background information on their natural history. To date, this required bringing about half a dozen books, without pictures, along into the field, or taking an animal back to base camp for identification (which is often impossible). Having struggled with these conditions ourselves, we resolved to put together a book that would be easy to use, convenient to take on excursions, and that would permit the identification of the vast majority of individual reptiles that are likely to be encountered.

It will be obvious that little information exists about the natural history of many species. Indeed, anyone can make new discoveries with relatively little effort, whether these are new distribution records, observations on habitat selection, feeding, reproduction, or behaviour. We encourage people to report their observations in appropriate journals, preferably accompanied by photographs of the animal and the subject of the discovery.

How to use this book

This book describes and illustrates most of the snakes, lizards, crocodiles and turtles that inhabit Peninsular (or West) Malaysia, Singapore and Thailand. We include nearby islands on the continental shelf, such as the Surin and Similan groups, Phuket, Tarutao, Langkawi, Penang, Tioman, the Samui group and Chaang, and the smaller islands near southeastern Thailand.

Since space is limited, it has not been possible to include all the 320 or so reptile species that are reported to occur in Peninsular Malaysia, Singapore and Thailand, and the adjacent seas. In making our selection of those to be included, we have emphasized the common, large, conspicuous, dangerous or biologically significant species. All terrestrial venomous snakes are included and all but three are illustrated. In general, the species not included are small, inconspicuous, rare, restricted in distribution, extremely similar to included species (such as various worm snakes and forest litter skinks), or unlikely to be encountered (most hydrophid sea snakes).

We have tried to arrange the species in the most convenient order for field identification. The overall arrangement is by family, more or less in traditional taxonomic order; within each family, we have grouped genera and species by superficial similarity and general habitat preference. While this system may be far from perfect, we believe it is of greater practical value to have, for example, the various genera of arboreal colubrid snakes in a single section, rather than have them scattered throughout the colubrid snake chapter as they would be if they were listed in alphabetical order or in any of the conflicting phylogenetic arrangements proposed. The index permits one to find a particular species instantly if the name is known, but when encountering an unknown animal in the wild, external appearance is the starting point for identification.

In each species account, we have aimed to provide enough external characters to permit identification with confidence. In many cases, especially after one becomes more familiar with the various species, animals can be identified from some distance in the field. In other cases, such as among the small forest skinks, precise identification is possible only by examining scale characters of the animal with a magnifying lens, a job that is best done while the animal is in a plastic bag.

The size indicated for each species is the maximum adult size, based on reliable reports. In many cases, especially for snakes and turtles, animals encountered are often much smaller. Snakes and crocodiles are measured along the entire length, from snout to tail tip. Lizard measurements are given as snout–vent length (SVL) plus total length (snout–vent plus tail) as many lizards have incomplete tails. Turtles are measured by the length of their carapace (upper shell), in a straight line for terrestrial and freshwater species, and over the curve for marine turtles.

In addition to morphological characteristics, information on distribution, altitude, habitat and other ecological features is given since it is often very helpful in identifying animals encountered in the field.

Reptile habitats in Peninsular Malaysia, Singapore and Thailand

The region covered by this guide extends over a great range of environmental conditions, from the northern mountains to the southern rainforests and coral reefs. Northern Thailand is predominantly mountainous, reaching its highest point at 2,565m above mean sea level at the summit of Doi Inthanon. These geologically complex mountains continue southwards along the Thai-Myanmar border into Peninsular Malaysia. Between Phuket and Surat Thani in southern Thailand there is a break in this mountain spine, which limits the distribution of some species. Northeastern Thailand between the valleys of the Chao Phraya and Mekong rivers is an elevated plateau with extensive sandstone outcrops.

The region as a whole is in the tropical monsoon belt, and thus under the influence of winds alternating seasonally between northeast and southwest. Most of Thailand above the peninsula has a distinctly seasonal climate: the dry and cool season under the influence of northeastern winds from central Asia lasts from November to February; the hot season with occasional showers is from March to May; and the rainy season with almost daily rain showers stretches from May to October. The seasons may begin or end a month earlier or later in any particular year. During the rainy season, rain comes from the Andaman Sea with the southwest monsoon, but occasionally the tail end of a Pacific cyclone passes over Thailand, causing a heavy downpour after having lost most of its force during its crossing of the Annamitic Mountains between Vietnam and Laos.

The climate of the peninsula is less seasonal and rain can be expected at almost any time of the year. This is because the dry northeast monsoon absorbs enough moisture when passing over the South China Sea and Gulf of Thailand to give rain when ascending over the peninsular mountain spine. The total annual rainfall varies by region, approaching 3,000mm in the peninsula but only about 1,300mm in northern Thailand. The annual mean temperature varies around 25–28°C depending on location. In the southern islands there is little daily or seasonal variation, but fluctuations become more dramatic in mainland Thailand where temperatures can be as high as 44°C and as low as light frost level at higher elevations at winter dawn.

The patterns of vegetation and land use in the region have changed dramatically in recent history. Originally, nearly the entire area was covered by forest. At present, much less than half the land is still covered by forest or other long-term vegetation cover. The wide range of topographical and climatic conditions result in a variety of forest types. The climax vegetation of the peninsular region is tropical, broadleaved, evergreen forest, conveniently called rainforest: this type has multiple crown levels under a closed canopy, which creates a humid interior with sparse undergrowth. To the north, seasonal rainfall supports the deciduous forest types, which deal with the temporary water shortage by dropping their old leaves; a flush of new growth follows the first heavy showers. Mature, undamaged, deciduous forest is composed of a rich mixture of tree species that create a tall, closed canopy. As this canopy permits light to reach the forest floor in the dry season, a dense undergrowth of grass, herbs, shrubs and young trees flourishes. The dry fallen leaves, however, make this mixed deciduous forest susceptible to leaf-litter fires and a regular succession of annual forest fires gradually eliminates some tree species, eventually resulting in forest composed of fire-resistant species only. This resulting fire-climax forest is termed dry or deciduous dipterocarp forest, as it is strongly dominated by trees of the dipterocarp family. It is a low, open forest type with often sparse grassy undergrowth and little organic material in the soil, quite different from the original mixed deciduous forest.

In addition to these major vegetation types, local conditions create opportunities for other vegetation types. Many are associated with water, such as lowland swamps and swamp forest, evergreen gallery forests along streams in otherwise dry areas, mangrove forest, and beach vegetation. Water itself forms habitats such as rivers, estuaries, mud-flats, rocky coasts and coral reefs. Mountains provide other habitats, such as montane broadleaf evergreen forest, pine forest, and the specialized vegetation of cliffs and crags.

This great diversity of vegetation types, altitude, climatic conditions and microhabitats offers a variety of environments that animals can inhabit. The long history of range expansions and contractions, isolation, speciation and extinction, and the presence of the rich fauna of the Indo-Burmese, the southern Chinese and the Malay archipelago regions as sources of immigrants, together make the flora and fauna of mainland Southeast Asia very rich and diverse. The diversity of snakes and other reptiles is correspondingly rich and diverse.

Finding, identifying and recording reptiles

There are few places in Peninsular Malaysia, Singapore or Thailand where there are no reptiles to see. Even in the middle of great cities some geckos, fence lizards, skinks and snakes can be found. However, to find more than the common species that live happily in human presence, one must visit natural habitats. All three countries have extensive national parks, together encompassing a wide range of habitat types. Meanwhile, other areas such as agricultural lands, plantations, beaches, wastelands, city parks, temple gardens, and road margins are home to a sometimes surprising diversity of reptile species.

Keen eyes alert to movement will spot many moving animals. At regular intervals take a rest from walking and use the time to look around you to see immobile animals. Wear inconspicuous clothes. Sound is often a very good indicator of the presence of herpetofauna. Once the sound of a startled animal running or jumping away has alerted you to its presence, you should carefully look for other animals. There will be thousands of false alarms caused by large grasshoppers, birds, rodents and others, but with time one learns to differentiate between the smooth, continuous sound of a sliding snake, the steady, clumsy sound of a tortoise, and the interrupted spurts of a lizard. A monitor lizard in tall grass can be heard a surprising distance away. Calling geckos can unwittingly guide the naturalist.

Snakes are difficult to find in most areas, but as a general rule pay particular attention to dry spots in wet areas and, conversely, search the moist spots in dry regions. Check where frogs call along a pond or stream edge; often a snake will be hunting nearby.

Lizards are usually seen skittering off the trail. The best way to view gliding lizards is by quietly standing or sitting in one place in the forest and carefully scanning the nearby tree trunks; binoculars are very helpful. Movements will betray foraging animals, while occasionally one may see the flash of a brightly coloured dewlap or the profile of a gliding lizard silhouetted against the sky. Their immediate response to disturbance is to move higher up on the other side of the tree trunk. Geckos are relatively easy to find at night by torchlight. Often they can be blinded in the light, allowing one to view and photograph them at very close range without any need to handle them.

When looking for animals, be sure not to damage the habitat. Stripping all bark from a fallen tree trunk may yield one or two geckos, but it also makes countless invertebrates plus those geckos homeless. Rocks and branches should be carefully replaced in their original positions, without crushing any of the creatures living below them. Snake-hooks, rather than for handling the snakes themselves, are very useful for moving branches, leaf piles, and so on, without danger to one's hands from scorpion stings, snake-bites and other animal defences.

Do not disturb animals and their habitat in places where this is not permitted, such as national parks and wildlife sanctuaries.

In some cases, it is necessary to catch an animal to examine it closely for identification. **Do not** attempt to handle any snake unless you are absolutely certain that it is not venomous. Large monitor lizards, crocodiles, and soft-shelled turtles of all sizes can inflict substantial damage when they bite and should be left undisturbed. **Be very gentle**. When catching lizards, make sure you do not touch the tail, as some species shed their tails as a distraction almost as soon as they are touched; they can break their tails by themselves and do not need the catcher to physically pull the tail.

Plastic bags and a torch are essential tools to find and carefully view small reptiles, while a ruler or measuring tape, a transparent plastic box, a magnifying lens, a snake-hook, binoculars and a camera are also useful. A notebook and pen complete the field equipment; regular note-taking not only builds up an often impressive personal record of one's observations, but can provide valuable scientific data. Any substantial field notes should include the following data: date and time; location; either species (including confirmations – note which diagnostic features were checked), or a description of the animal if unidentified; habitat (vegetation type, soil, altitude, and so on); weather conditions; microhabitat; activity of the animal; and any other information that may seem relevant.

Lizards are best placed in a rigid clear plastic box with lid for viewing. By holding the box sideways, the animal will usually slide to the side, making it easy to measure body and tail length in a straight line by holding a tape alongside, and to look at scales and other details with a magnifying lens. Plastic bags and boxes are ideal to examine the feet of geckos in minute detail. After examination, release the animal exactly where you found it, unless that place is clearly accidental and unsuitable (such as a concrete drain or a road).

We strongly discourage collecting and preserving live specimens. Not only is this illegal in many places, but it often serves little purpose. This book provides all relevant data to identify an animal; proper photographs provide sufficient confirmation in most cases. In cases of serious doubt, the best course of action is to consult a specialist, for example the curator of a national reference collection. If the specialist cannot identify the animal from photographs, it may be worth an official field trip to investigate the animals. Visitors should be aware that many species of reptile may not be exported from their native countries and may not be brought into other countries without proper documentation. Animal smuggling is considered a serious crime by many customs departments and penalties can be severe.

Photographing reptiles is a fascinating hobby in its own right. The facts that most species are small, shy and alert and many are nocturnal pose some serious challenges in the choice of camera equipment. A single-lens reflex camera with a lens permitting close focusing is an absolute necessity for satisfactory pictures of anything smaller than a large tortoise. Wide-angle lenses provide good depth of focus for animals that allow one to come close, while medium-range telelenses work best for agile and alert lizards. Auto-focus is often useful, but is not essential; especially at close range and with animals whose head is not in the centre of the picture, manual focusing gives better control. Often it is easier to focus by moving one's head and camera backwards or forwards, rather than by turning the lens ring. If in doubt about correct exposure, bracket by taking an extra underexposed picture with the aperture closed one stop further and an overexposed shot with the aperture opened one extra stop, as well as one at the setting suggested by your light meter.

There is rarely sufficient light when taking pictures of reptiles in the wild, so a flash is very useful. To avoid difficult calculations of flash output level at often very close range, a Through The Lens (TTL) dedicated flash, where the camera measures how much light comes through the lens and signals the flash to stop at the appropriate level, is almost essential. A macro ring-flash mounted around the front of the lens, or a flash cord allowing a normal flash with a diffusor to be held above the animal, make the light seem much more natural. The choices between print or slide film, and between high or low film speeds, are matters of individual preference. Numerous good books and magazines deal with wildlife and close-up photography, and up-to-date information on equipment and techniques are easy to find in any good bookshop and library.

With patience and some luck it is possible to get good pictures of wild animals in their natural habitat. Aim to get the animal's eye in focus. Patience is often rewarded with a better picture, especially with turtles. If the animal permits, take photographs of the whole animal first and then go as close as your equipment allows. Portraits bring out the delicate beauty of most reptiles. Puzzle-pictures ('Where's the snake's tail?') are fun when you get a set of prints back from processing, but they have no long-term value except perhaps as habitat indications. If one photographically documents a specimen for later identification or confirmation, one needs: a general picture of the whole animal; a close-up of the side of the head; a photograph of the animal's ventral side; and any other diagnostic features. Do not forget to note the locality and habitat of the animal, and record measurements such as length, scale counts, and so on. Finally, remember that photographic film is much cheaper than the time and money it takes to find an animal: take those extra pictures.

Conservation and protection of reptiles in Peninsular Malaysia, Singapore and Thailand

Reptiles have been used by humans for a long time and for a variety of purposes. Consumption of turtles, large lizards, snakes and reptile eggs has a long history, as has the use of prepared reptile parts in traditional medicine. Harvesting of crocodiles and certain species of snake and lizard for leather production has had serious effects on some species. The international trade in pets results in the export of numerous small turtles, snakes and lizards. Yet the greatest cause of declining reptile populations is the loss of natural habitats as ever more land is settled and cultivated.

Concern about declining reptile populations has resulted in a variety of measures aimed at protecting existing populations and preventing further losses. Each of the countries in the region has legislation protecting its natural heritage, including reptiles. All species in protected areas such as national parks and wildlife sanctuaries are protected from disturbance. In addition, many reptile species are specifically protected under national legislation and their collection is either regulated or prohibited outright.

International trade in many endangered and/or economically important species is regulated under the Convention on International Trade in Endangered Species (CITES). Species may be listed in Appendix 1 of CITES which prohibits all international trade, in Appendix 2 in which case an export licence from the country of origin is required, or not listed so that international trade is not regulated.

The lists of species included under national and international protective legislation are reviewed every few years, and changes are made according to the best available information. For details of which species are protected, and to what extent, one should contact the responsible authority in the country concerned.

Snake-bite

The following section should be a complete waste of space because most cases of snake-bite result from humans intentionally disturbing and threatening a snake. Venomous snakes do not enjoy biting people; they react to a perceived serious threat to their own safety. Most snakes will flee, undetected; when flight is not possible, they will warn the intruder by hissing or threat displays, such as rearing up and flattening the neck. Nobody should attempt to handle any animals of which he or she is not absolutely certain, both in terms of what it is and how dangerous it might be. Admire it from a safe distance, which may be as much as several metres in the case of spitting cobras.

The best prevention of snake-bite is to watch carefully where you put your feet and hands and to give snakes the space they deserve.

First-aid treatment for snake-bites

Traditional first-aid methods for bites from venomous snakes were to apply a tourniquet or to cut into the bite site. These practices are now seriously discredited and may be more dangerous than the bite itself.

At present, medical professionals working with snake-bite victims agree that the best emergency treatment is to limit the blood flow from the bite site to the rest of the body while getting the patient to hospital.

- First and foremost, the victim should try to relax. Take relief from the facts that most snakes are not venomous and that many venomous snakes do not always inject venom with defensive bites.
- Remember what kind of snake bit you. Bring this book with you to the hospital and point out the snake. Do not try to kill the snake and certainly do not bring it along alive.
- Wash the bite site with clean water to avoid infection.
- To slow the flow of blood from the bite, the affected body part should be tightly wrapped with a long elastic bandage (the type normally used to support sprained ankles, available at any good pharmacy). If such a bandage is not available, any strip of cloth will do in an emergency. Tight elastic bandages restrict blood flow without completely cutting off the circulation, which can result in tissue destruction. If the toes or fingers turn blue, the bandage is too tight. You should be able, just, to insert a finger under the bandage. Not only the bite site itself, but also a good part of the limb above and below the bite site should be wrapped. Fit a splint to further immobilize the bite site. Remove any rings, bracelets or wristwatches from the bitten limb, as swelling may occur.
- Next, the victim should be transported to hospital as soon as possible without exerting the person. Transport by car is best. If no roads or vehicles are available, carry the victim or walk slowly; do not run. If in a national park, ask an official to send a radio message to the hospital.
- Watch the victim closely for signs of breathing difficulties, as the venom of some snakes impairs respiration. Be prepared to give artificial respiration if necessary. If the victim is barely conscious, place him on his side to ease breathing and prevent choking if he vomits. At the hospital, trained professionals will administer the best possible treatment.

Two of the three cobra species in the region have the ability to spit venom into the eyes of an attacker. Their aim is amazingly accurate and they can easily reach 2m. The venom will cause temporary blindness. Wash the eyes immediately with clean water and there will not be any serious results. It is prudent to regard all cobras as spitters and keep more than 2m away.

BLIND SNAKES (Family Typhlopidae)

Members of this family are usually small and sometimes mistaken for worms. All species are burrowers in soil, leaf litter and decaying logs. They are active at night and sometimes seen above ground, but they are most often encountered when digging in surface debris. The head is short and indistinct, and the body is cylindrical and of uniform diameter throughout; the tail is quite short and ends in a spine. The scales are smooth, shiny, and the same size all around the body. There are no large ventral shields. The eyes are tiny and may be invisible. These small snakes prey primarily on insect larvae and pupae. Egg-laying and live-bearing species are known. About a dozen members of this family are native to our area; they differ in the number of scale rows around the body, the arrangement of scales on the head and features of the colour pattern.

Common Blind, or **Flowerpot, Snake**

Ramphotyphlops braminus to 23cm

The eyes of this wide-ranging blind snake are visible. The rostral is relatively narrow, accounting for 20–33% of head width. It is nearly uniform in colour, being dark brown to black above but somewhat lighter below. The snout, anal region, and tip of tail are usually pale. The Common Blind Snake occurs from sea level up to 1,640m, and is found under the surface of the soil, under surface debris, or in rotten logs. It feeds mainly on the larvae of ants and termites. This is the only known parthenogenic snake species; all individuals are females and males are unknown. Females produce clutches of 1–7 eggs, measuring 2 × 6mm, without fertilization; all eggs develop into females. This species is found throughout Thailand, Peninsular Malaysia, and Singapore. It has also been recorded from Africa, the Middle East, the remainder of tropical Asia and parts of eastern temperate Asia, from islands across the Pacific and from Mexico and the United States.

Diard's Blind Snake *Typhlops diardi* to 43cm

Mark O'Shea

Diard's Blind Snake is one of the largest blind snakes, both in length and thickness. The rostral is 25–40% of the head's width, and the eye is visible. The upper side of the body is dark brown; the sides and belly are much lighter in colour. There is no sharp line of demarcation between dark and light colours. It lives at 150–1,525m, under soil or surface debris and in rotten logs; it is sometimes seen on the surface after heavy rains. There are 4–14 eggs per clutch. This snake occurs in Thailand north of the peninsula, in Myanmar and in adjacent regions but it is displaced by Mueller's Blind Snake in Malaysia and Indonesia.

Mueller's Blind Snake *Typhlops muelleri* to 45cm

Ulrich Manthey

Mueller's Blind Snake is another relatively long, thick-bodied blind snake. The rostral is 33–40% of the head's width and the eye is visible. The relatively stout body is blackish-olive to brown above, yellowish-white to white below and with a sharp line of demarcation between the colours. This snake is found in lowlands and hill country under the surface of the soil, among surface litter or in rotten logs. Clutches contain 5–14 eggs. Mueller's Blind Snake occurs in most of Southeast Asia, from Myanmar and Vietnam to Singapore and Kalimantan.

PYTHONS (Family Boidae)

The head is distinct, with large shields that are sometimes fragmented. The rostral, anterior supralabials, and anterior and posterior infralabials have pits leading to heat-sensing nerves that help these snakes find prey. The pupil is vertical. The body scales are smooth; the ventral shields are rather narrow. Spurs – remnants of rear legs – flank the anal shield. The three pythons found in our area are nocturnal and prey on warm-blooded animals.

Reticulated Python *Python reticulatus* reputedly to 1,000cm

The head and stout body are tan or yellowish-tan. A network of black lines extends along the top of the body and down the sides where the lines widen and encircle white spots. A black line extends from the snout over the crown to the neck. Black lines also extend from the eye to the base of the jaw. This handsome snake is iridescent in sunlight. The Reticulated Python primarily inhabits humid forests up to 1,500m, but is also at home in orchards, agricultural lands and human habitation. It is essentially terrestrial but is a good climber. This snake is a powerful constrictor and feeds on almost any mammal it can overpower, ranging from mice to deer and pigs. Consequently, **large adults can be dangerous to humans**. It is oviparous and prolific: a record clutch of 124 eggs has been recorded. Incubation requires approximately three months; hatchlings average 55cm and resemble the parents. This python can still be found throughout Thailand, Malaysia, Singapore and beyond to Myanmar, the Philippines and Flores.

Short, or **Blood, Python**
Python curtus brongersmai to 275cm

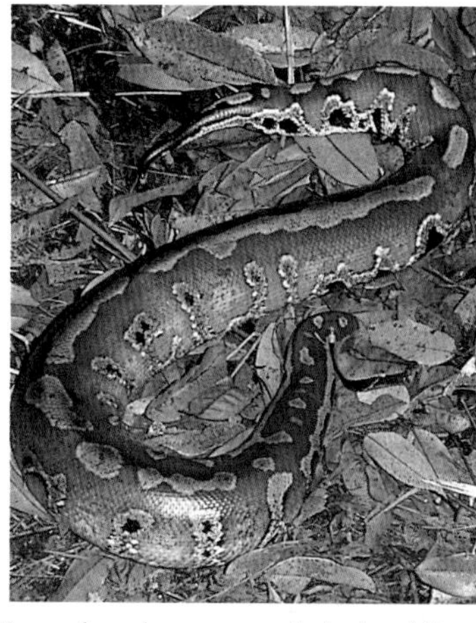
Wolfgang Grossmann

This species is the smallest and least common python in our area. Its head is proportionally small. The thick body is dark brown to brick red with irregular, dark-centred, light blotches on the flanks. The Blood Python is fairly aquatic, occurring along river banks in forested areas up to 900m, often in streams or partially buried under mud or vegetation. It waits in ambush to seize its prey, primarily rodents and aquatic birds. Clutches of 10–15 eggs have been reported; the hatchlings are about 35cm long but otherwise resemble adults. This beautiful subspecies inhabits southern Thailand, West Malaysia, Singapore, Banka and eastern Sumatra; other subspecies occur in western Sumatra, Kalimantan and East Malaysia.

Burmese Python *Python molurus bivittatus* to 600cm

This large attractive snake has a stout yellowish to light-brown body. A series of black-edged, dark-brown blotches is superimposed on the lighter ground colour. The top of the head has a pale arrow-shaped mark. The belly is white or cream. This Python lives in forested plains and hills up to 900m. This is a powerful ambushing constrictor and **adults are dangerous**. Eggs are laid in clutches of 30–50, hatchlings are 50–79cm. It occurs disjunctly in mainland tropical Asia including Thailand north of the Kra Isthmus as well as in Kalimantan, Java, Sumbawa and Sulawesi.

SUNBEAM SNAKES (Family Xenopeltidae)

The depressed head is indistinct and covered with large shields. The eye is small, the pupil vertical. Smooth scales cover the cylindrical body, the ventral shields are well developed and the tail is short.

Sunbeam Snake *Xenopeltis unicolor* to 125cm

Wolfgang Grossmann

(Above) *Newborn showing white collar*

The body is black to chocolate brown above and very iridescent; when struck by sunlight, the scales glisten beautifully, hence the vernacular name. The belly is white. Hatchlings are identical to adults except for a white collar around the neck. This nocturnal, semi-burrowing species is found in humid plains and hills up to 1,300m. This relatively slow-moving snake feeds on a variety of prey including rodents, birds, lizards, and other snakes. Oviparous, clutches of 6–17 eggs are known. This attractive snake is common in most of Southeast Asia.

PIPE SNAKES (Family Aniliidae)

The head is small, indistinct, and with large symmetrical shields. The eyes are small. The stout cylindrical body can be flattened; the pointed tail is very short. The body scales are smooth and the ventral shields only slightly enlarged.

Red-tailed Pipe Snake *Cylindrophis ruffus* to 100cm

The body is black to dark purple, the belly has white crossbands, and the subcaudal area is bright orange-red. Young are paler and have distinct white bands around the body. This snake inhabits humid lowland areas. It is usually found under the surface of the soil, under surface debris, in soft mud or in rafts of floating vegetation during the day, but it may be found foraging on the surface at night. It preys on other snakes and eels. Up to 13 young are born, on average 20cm long. When threatened it tucks its head under its body and bluffs by flattening and raising its tail to show the bold coloration. It is common throughout Southeast Asia.

FILE SNAKES (Family Acrochordidae)

Theses snakes have loose, hanging skin which is covered with small rough scales to grip fish during the swallowing process. They are totally aquatic and lack enlarged ventral shields. The small eyes have vertically elliptic pupils. The nostrils are valved to prevent water from entering when submerged and are located at the top of the snout.

File Snake *Acrochordus granulatus* to 100cm

Mark O'Shea

The File Snake has a prominent fold of skin extending along the centre of the belly; the tapering tail is slightly compressed. The head is dark. The body pattern consists of alternating white and black or dark-brown bands, which are broad on the back but narrow on the sides and may extend across the belly. This nocturnal species inhabits various coastal habitats. It feeds predominantly on small fish. A litter of 5–10 young, averaging 22cm, is born after about six months' gestation. Because of its habitat and markings, it is often confused with venomous sea snakes. It ranges from India to northern Australia and to Hainan.

Elephant-trunk Snake *Acrochordus javanicus* to 290cm

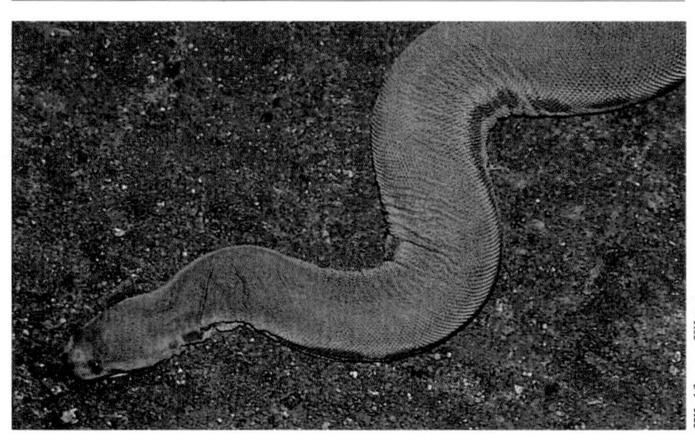

Wolfgang Wüster

The head of this odd snake is short and blunt. The thick body is olive-brown to grey-brown with a faintly marbled, black pattern on the sides. The ventral surface is lighter than above and lacks a prominent central skin fold. The Elephant-trunk Snake lives in slow-moving water, either fresh or brackish, including estuaries and freshwater rivers and canals. It feeds on eels and other fish. Females can be prolific, producing litters of 18–48 young of up to 29cm length. This snake inhabits the waterways of the lower central plain and southern Thailand, Malaysia, Cambodia, Vietnam and Indonesia.

VIPERS (Family Viperidae)

These snakes have a pair of very long fangs in the front of the mouth, which are used to deliver venom deep into prey or predators. When the mouth is closed the fangs fold back against the roof of the mouth. Representatives of two subfamilies of the Viperidae occur in our area of interest; most species belong to the subfamily Crotalinae, whose members are characterized by a large temperature-sensitive pit between the nostril and the eye. The subfamily Viperinae, represented here only by the Siamese Russell's Viper, lacks this pit. All regional vipers have vertical pupils and a large, triangular head distinctly set off from the neck; all except the Malayan Pit-viper have small scales on the crown of the head, and most have strongly keeled head and body scales.

Siamese Russell's Viper

Daboia russellii siamensis (*Vipera russellii*) to 150cm

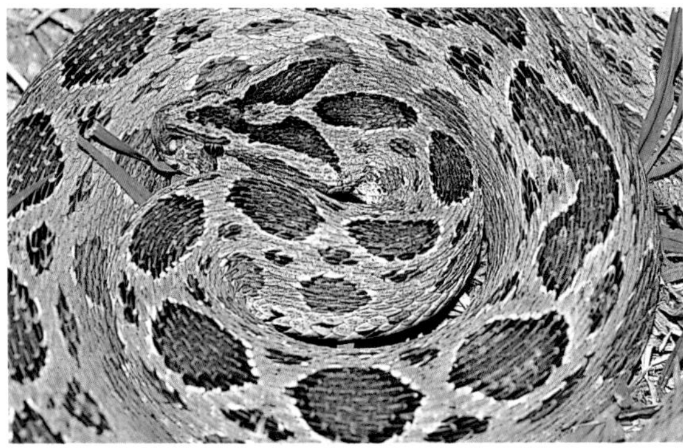

Wolfgang Wüster

Merel J. Cox

The stout body is tan with a series of multi-coloured blotches of variable shape and size. All, however, are dark brown with a black inner edge and a white outer edge. The same blotches appear on the crown of the head, although they are smaller there. The tail is striped. Terrestrial and nocturnal, this subspecies is found in open country up to 2,000m. It avoids dense vegetation and can be found coiled in open shelters. When threatened, it makes a very loud, continuous hissing sound that can be quite alarming. Ovoviviparous, litters of up to 63 neonates are known, measuring 24–30cm but otherwise resembling adults. **Venomous and potentially fatal.** It occurs localized in central and eastern Thailand, Myanmar, southern China, Taiwan and Java.

Malayan Pit-viper *Calloselasma rhodostoma* to 100cm

Wolfgang Wüster

(Right) Hatchling

Lawan Chanhome

Jarujin Nabhitabhata

Pale colour form

The head has nine prominent, symmetric, unfragmented head shields. The snout is turned up and pointed. A ridge extends from the eye to the snout. The body is moderately stout, the scales smooth. The pattern consists of 19–31 dark, triangular markings on a light to dark reddish or purplish-brown background. This terrestrial snake prefers rather dry, forested lowlands, but has been found up to 2,000m. Nocturnal and preferring high air humidity, it preys on frogs, toads, rodents, birds, and other snakes from ambush. Females lay clutches of 13–30 eggs which they guard during the five to seven weeks of incubation. The 13–20cm long hatchlings are similar to adults except for their bright yellow tail, which is elevated and moved to lure prey. **Venomous and potentially fatal**. This snake is found throughout Thailand and the northern states of Peninsular Malaysia.

White-lipped Pit-viper

Trimeresurus albolabris albolabris to 100cm

The body of this attractive viper is fairly stout, the scales keeled. The head and body are green, the chin, throat and belly greenish or yellowish-white. Males have a white stripe on the first body scale row which is indistinct or absent on females. The tail is reddish-brown. It prefers open country below 400m, sometimes inhabits urban areas. It hunts mice, birds, lizards and frogs at night on the ground and spends daytime resting in vegetation. Litters comprise 7–16 miniature replicas of adults, 12–18cm long. **Venomous and dangerous**, this species is responsible for many snake-bite cases. Widely distributed in tropical Asia, it occurs throughout Thailand.

Big-eyed Pit-viper *Trimeresurus macrops* to 72cm

Wolfgang Grossmann

The large golden-yellow eyes distinguish this species. The head is short, rounded, but still triangular; the body is slender and the scales are keeled. The upper head and body are bluish-green. The ventrals are bluish and the tail reddish-brown, but the subcaudals are slightly bluish. This nocturnal viper can be found on the ground at dusk or in the early morning hours hunting for small animals. Females give birth to 6–12 young per litter, each a miniature replica of an adult. This **venomous and dangerous** snake occurs in most of Thailand north of the peninsula and in Cambodia and southern Vietnam.

Pope's Pit-viper *Trimeresurus popeiorum* to 82cm

Wolfgang Wüster

The top of the head and body are medium green, the ventrals pale green. A white stripe, sometimes bordered ventrally with dark red or orange, extends along the first body scale row. Occasionally males have a white postocular stripe. The tail is reddish-brown. The head scales are smooth, the body scales keeled. Pope's Pit-viper is nocturnal and is most frequently found on low bushes and shrubs. It is most abundant in hilly or mountainous terrain at elevations between 900m and 1,500m. Litters contain 7–12 young which are each 12–18cm long. **Venomous and dangerous**. It is found in northern and southern Thailand, West Malaysia as far south as Pulau Tioman, northeastern India, Myanmar, Indo-China, Sumatra and East Malaysia.

Bamboo Pit-viper or **Chinese Green Tree-viper** *Trimeresurus stejnegeri* to 112cm

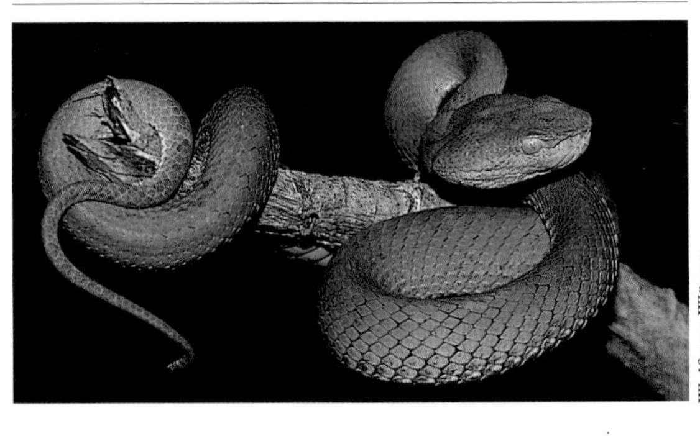

Wolfgang Wüster

The Bamboo Pit-viper is externally identical to Pope's Pit-viper, but its hemipenis has a fundamentally different structure. Consequently, while they are genuinely different species, only males can be identified with certainty. It inhabits montane forests up to 2,845m. Nocturnal and semi-arboreal, it is often found resting or foraging near mountain streams. Frogs may be their primary prey, but small mammals, birds and lizards are also eaten. Litters of 3–10 are born; the newborn resemble adults. **Venomous and dangerous**. It occurs in isolated areas in Thailand, as well as Myanmar and much of China; it has been reported from Cambodia and Vietnam.

Indonesian Pit-viper *Trimeresurus hageni* to 96cm

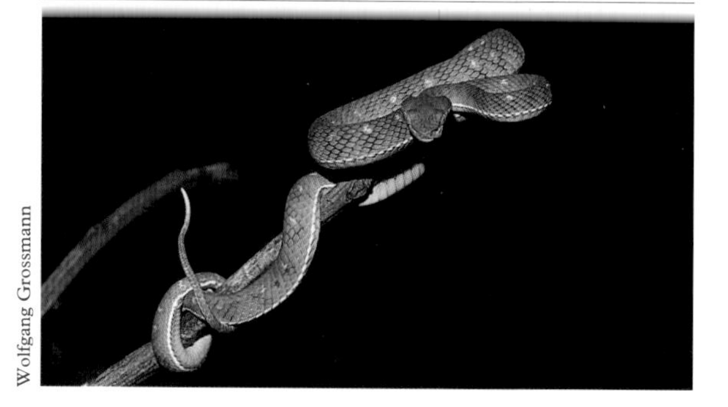

Wolfgang Grossmann

The head and body scales of this pit-viper are uniform green. A white line extends along the two lowest flank scale rows, bordered below by a dark line or spots. There is a pink streak behind the eye while the body may bear pink spots which merge with the pinkish tail. It is found in lowlands and forested hills up to 1,000m. Females produce clutches of 13–17 eggs; hatchlings are about 24cm. **Venomous and dangerous**. It inhabits the southern provinces of Thailand, West Malaysia and Indonesia east to Sumatra and Bangka. The similar SUMATRAN PIT-VIPER (*T. sumatranus*) shares part of this range; its head scales have black borders, and dark bars usually cross the body.

Kanburi Pit-viper *Trimeresurus kanburiensis* to 70cm

Wolfgang Wüster

This attractive little viper has a purplish-brown head with small olive-green blotches. The body has keeled scales and a pattern of narrow alternating, zigzagging bands of olive-green and purplish-brown. A white stripe appears near the 15th ventral and continues along the edge of the first body scale row through the vent and into the colours of the tail. The ventral surface is yellowish-green. This nocturnal viper inhabits evergreen forests up to 1,000m. Litters of 12–16 have been recorded; the young are 16–20cm long. **Venomous and dangerous**. It has been found only in the west and south of Thailand.

Mangrove, or **Shore, Pit-viper**
Trimeresurus purpureomaculatus to 105cm

Gernot Vogel

The head scales are tuberculate or keeled, and the crown is blackish-brown. The relatively stout body bears strongly keeled scales and is greenish-yellow with dark blotches, wide above and narrower on the sides. The ventral scales are white with black edges; the subcaudals are predominantly black. A second colour variety is uniformly purplish-brown. This nocturnal snake resides in mangrove forests, where it is often observed on low bushes. It feeds on lizards, frogs and other small animals. Litters contain 7–14 babies of about 24cm. **Venomous and dangerous**, it has a reputation for being quick to strike. This snake inhabits southern Thailand, Peninsular Malaysia, Singapore, Tenasserim and Sumatra.

Wagler's Pit-viper or **Temple Viper**
Tropidolaemus wagleri to 100cm

Wolfgang Wüster

Gernot Vogel

Juvenile

This handsome snake's head is very large and the body stout. The yellow and green body bears white, red, dark green or black spots or cross bands. The top of the head is black with green markings, the ventral shields are white with black edges and the tail is black. Juveniles number up to 41 per litter and are bright green with red-and-white spots or crossbars. This nocturnal viper is arboreal and lives among low vegetation in forests, including mangrove, from sea level to 1,200m. **Venomous and dangerous**. This snake resides in southern Thailand, West Malaysia, Singapore, parts of Indonesia and the Philippines.

Bornean Pit-viper *Trimeresurus puniceus* to 64cm

Merel J. Cox

This unusual little snake has a spatula-shaped, slightly upturned snout that protrudes beyond the chin. An elevated ridge extends from the eye to the snout. The body is short and stout. The head scales are smooth, the body scales feebly keeled. Both the head and body are reddish-brown; the body has an uneven light pattern. The belly is mottled brown and darker than the dorsal surface. This is a nocturnal forest species found at elevations up to 1,450m. Females incubate clutches of 7–14 eggs, and hatchlings resemble adults. **Venomous and dangerous**. This snake is found in southern Thailand, throughout Malaysia, Borneo, Sumatra and in Java.

Mountain Pit-viper *Ovophis monticola convictus* to 100cm

Don Wells

The stout body is brown, yellowish or grey-brown, with one or two dorsal series of large, squarish, dark-brown blotches. The top of the head is blackish-brown; there is a brown stripe behind the eye, and the chin and throat are light mottled with brown. The small head scales and the body scales are smooth. This nocturnal viper is a terrestrial highland species occurring at 610–1,750m, often under forest litter and stones. Its clutches contain 5–18 eggs; the 18–20cm long hatchlings resemble adults. **Venomous and dangerous**. This snake inhabits mountains in northern, western and southern Thailand and Peninsular Malaysia, and ranges to Nepal, Taiwan and Sumatra.

ELAPID SNAKES (Family Elapidae)

These snakes have fixed hollow fangs on the front of the upper jaws. All elapid snake species have specialized venom-producing glands which produce highly toxic venom often fatal to man. Indeed, this family includes species considered to be the most dangerous in the world. None has a loreal scale. All 14 species of elapids in our area are oviparous and most are terrestrial.

King Cobra *Ophiophagus hannah* to 585cm

Wolfgang Wüster

Piboon Jintakune

Banded juvenile pattern

This majestic snake is by far the largest venomous snake in the world. The head bears large shields, the hood is long and narrow. The body has smooth scales. Adults vary in colour from uniform light green-grey to light green or orange-yellow with darker bands, while uniform dark grey to black individuals occur. The hood may bear chevron marks or be unpatterned. Active by day and at night, this impressive terrestrial snake inhabits forests and plantations up to 2,135m, often near streams. It preys on other snakes and occasionally on large lizards. The female builds a nest and guards the clutch, which comprises 20–51 eggs. Hatchlings measure 43–48cm and are black with yellow bands and a yellow chevron on the neck. The large venom glands produce a **very potent neurotoxin that is fatal if untreated**, making this one of the most dangerous snakes world-wide, yet because of its preference for undisturbed forests and its behaviour, few, if any, accidents occur. Most King Cobra sightings are no more than a glimpse of a swiftly-disappearing large snake, but when cornered this agile and intelligent snake will rear up the anterior third of its body and spread its neck. The King Cobra ranges throughout Southeast Asia and also inhabits India and southern China.

Cobras (Genus *Naja*)

When at rest, cobras' heads are not very distinct from the neck, but when threatened and on the defensive the ribs in the neck can be expanded to create the famous cobra 'hood'. The head shields are large, the eyes are moderate, the pupil round. The body is cylindrical with smooth scales. Cobras are primarily nocturnal and terrestrial snakes, found on plains and in mountains. They are adaptable, however – at home in agricultural lands and sometimes found near human habitation. Two of the three species in our area are 'spitting cobras': when threatened, they can spray venom into the eyes of their tormentors and cause temporary blindness; they will then make their escape. If the eyes are washed immediately, there are no serious results. However, it is best to regard all cobras as spitters and keep more than 2m away. Cobras are oviparous. They hunt for amphibians, other snakes, birds, and small mammals.

Monocellate Cobra *Naja kaouthia* to 200cm

Wolfgang Wüster

Wolfgang Wüster

Typical hood pattern

This 'classical' cobra usually has a distinct mark on the neck hood, variable in shape but often like a monocle. The coloration varies widely as well: usually the body is medium to dark brown or grey-brown; many specimens are uniform, others slightly banded. The white throat has a pair of small lateral spots. The ventral coloration

Piboon Jintakune

Piboon Jintakune

Variations in hood patterns

varies, but there is usually a distinct dark band behind the throat, followed by a light band and another dark band; the rest of the venter is mottled with dark pigment. As the coloration is so variable, many forms have been considered to represent different species, but recent research has shown that all non-spitting cobras in the region represent just a single, variable species. The Monocellate Cobra inhabits plains and mountains up to 700m. It hunts toads, snakes, birds, and small mammals. By day it can be found in termite mounds, near human habitation and in a wide range of other hiding places. Females lay up to 45 eggs in a clutch. Hatchlings are 28–35cm long and miniature replicas of the parents including fully functional venom glands. This is not a spitting cobra but its bite is **venomous and potentially fatal**. It occurs throughout Thailand except in the north, in northern Peninsular Malaysia, northeastern India, southern China, Myanmar, Laos, Cambodia, and Vietnam.

Wolfgang Wüster

Pale colour variety ('Suphan Cobra') at ease

Indo-Chinese Spitting Cobra *Naja siamensis* to 160cm

Wolfgang Wüster

Piboon Jintakune

Merel J. Cox

The coloration and pattern of this fascinating snake are highly variable. The hood mark may be a monocle or U-, V-, or H-shaped; it is often faint or absent. In the black form, the body may be mottled irregularly with black and white, uniform black dorsally and ventrally, or predominantly white. The head is usually black. Hatchlings of the black form have only a slight hint of pattern, which develops as they mature. Some individuals of the olive form are olive-green or greyish-green and patternless, but most have a light U- or spectacle-shaped hood mark and a few have indistinct crossbands on the body. The head is greenish-brown. It inhabits lowlands and hill country. Females are known to produce 13–19 eggs per clutch, and the hatchlings are 20–32cm long. It is **a spitting cobra and its bite is potentially fatal.** This snake has been found in Thailand south to 13.5°N, as well as in Cambodia and southern Vietnam.

Equatorial Spitting Cobra *Naja sumatrana* to 160cm

Merel J. Cox

Wolfgang Wüster

The Equatorial Spitting Cobra occurs in yellow and black phases. In the yellow form, the body is yellow or yellowish-green with some black-edged scales. The head is dark yellow, the labials light yellow, the eyes are dark and prominent and the tongue is pink. The venter is pale yellow. Black forms are uniform black except for a lighter chin, throat and ventrals. In both colour forms a hood mark is absent. Juveniles generally resemble adults; those of the black form may have yellow bands, spots or ocelli. This cobra inhabits lowlands and forested uplands to 1,500m. It is often found in lowlands in Peninsular Malaysia where it replaces the Monocellate Cobra. Its diet includes lizards, rodents and other small prey. Clutches contain 6–23 eggs; hatchlings are about 28cm long. **The bite of this spitting cobra is potentially fatal**. The yellow form is more common in southern Thailand, the black form more common in West Malaysia and Singapore. This species also occurs in Sumatra, Borneo and nearby islands.

Malayan, or **Blue, Krait** *Bungarus candidus* to 144cm

Wolfgang Wüster

Black and white bands alternate along this krait's cylindrical body: there are 19–30 black body bands on, but not encircling, the body and seven to nine on the tail. Individual black scales often occur on the white bands that connect to the white belly. The head is grey-black, the supralabials a bit lighter. Like all kraits, it has smooth scales which are enlarged in the vertebral series. It inhabits forested areas up to 1,525m. It is nocturnal and preys primarily on other snakes. Females produce 4–10 eggs per year; hatchlings are 27–29cm. **Venomous and potentially fatal**. The Malayan Krait occurs throughout Thailand, Malaysia, Singapore, Indo-China and parts of Indonesia.

Banded Krait *Bungarus fasciatus* to 200cm

Wolfgang Wüster

The elevated vertebral ridge gives the Banded Krait a triangular body. Yellow and black bands of almost equal width encircle the body and tail; the body bears 14–32 black bands, the tail 2–5. The head is predominantly black, the supralabials yellow. Hatchlings have grey rather than yellow bands. This krait prefers dry open country and forested lowland but it is recorded at 2,300m. It preys on small mammals, lizards and snakes. Clutches comprise 4–14 eggs; hatchlings are 25–40cm. Sluggish during the day, active and dangerous at night, it is **venomous and potentially fatal**. This is the most common krait in our area; it occurs throughout Thailand, Malaysia, Singapore and nearby regions.

Red-headed Krait *Bungarus flaviceps* to 190cm

The Red-headed Krait is a very beautiful snake. Its head and tail are bright red, the stocky body is black and shiny. There are small white specks along the vertebral ridge and sides of the body. The white of the belly extends to the first few body scales; the subcaudals are red. Hatchlings are unrecorded, but presumed to resemble adults. This rare krait inhabits forests from sea level to 914m. It feeds on other snakes and skinks. This nocturnal snake is **venomous and potentially fatal**. It occurs in Tenasserim, peninsular Thailand south of Ratchaburi, Peninsular Malaysia, Sumatra, Bangka, East Malaysia and Kalimantan.

Blue Long-glanded, or **Blue Malaysian, Coral Snake** *Maticora bivirgata flaviceps* to 140cm

Piboon Jintakune

This beautiful snake has a red tail and head, while the body is very dark iridescent blue. It bears a narrow blue or purplish line along the two lower body scales. The ventral surface is red. This rare, nocturnal snake is found in lowland forested areas up to 500m. It preys on other snakes and probably lizards and frogs. Clutches of 1–3 eggs are known. This snake inhabits southern Thailand, West Malaysia, Singapore, Myanmar and parts of Indonesia. The BROWN LONG-GLANDED CORAL SNAKE (*M. intestinalis*) has nearly the same range. It has a faded red vertebral stripe and only reaches 50cm.

Small-spotted Coral Snake *Calliophis maculiceps* to 47cm

Raynoo Homhual Cox

The head of this variable snake is brownish-black, the body dark orange or reddish-brown. The body pattern may consist of widely separated dots on the flanks, irregular large dots, a black twisted segmented pattern on the vertebral ridge, a black vertebral stripe, or no body pattern at all. A black band encircles the base of the tail and another the tail tip. The venter is pink; the subcaudals are black and white in varying proportions. This nocturnal snake is generally found under debris, logs and similar cover in forests up to 1,000m. A clutch of 2 eggs is known. It preys upon small snakes, particularly *Typhlops*, and lizards. It occurs throughout Thailand, northern Peninsular Malaysia, Tenasserim and southern Indo-China. **Venomous and dangerous**. The GREY CORAL SNAKE (*C. gracilis*) has a grey body with black vertebral stripe and black spots along the flank, and the venter has black and white bars. It occurs localized in extreme southern Thailand, Peninsular Malaysia, Singapore and Sumatra.

McClelland's Coral Snake *Calliophis macclellandi* to 80cm

Gernot Vogel

The head of this colourful snake is black; behind the eyes is a broad ivory band followed by a broad black band. The body is reddish dorsally with a series of 23–40 narrow, black, light-edged bands crossing it, some incomplete on the flanks. The tail has two to six black bands. The chin is cream; the venter is yellowish with black marks. This beautiful snake inhabits lowlands to areas above 1,000m where it is usually found under forest litter. It hunts other snakes and lizards at night. This coral snake ranges through the eastern Himalayan foothills, and in Thailand occurs in the northern and eastern regions.

SEA KRAITS (Genus *Laticauda*)

Sea Kraits spend much of their time in the ocean but, unlike members of the family Hydrophiidae, they come ashore roughly once a day and they are oviparous and deposit their eggs on land. Their heads are barely distinct. They have large head shields, round pupils, and their nostrils are on the sides of the snout. The cylindrical bodies are covered with smooth scales, and the tail is vertically compressed and shaped like an oar. They have wide ventral shields to facilitate movement on land. Eels comprise the bulk of the prey. Two sea krait species occur along the western coast of the Malay Peninsula.

Yellow-lipped Sea Krait *Laticauda colubrina* to 150cm

Harold Voris & Robert Stuebing

The head of this sea krait is black with yellow, creamy or grey snout and labials. The body is blue-grey and encircled by 24–64 black bands, with 3–5 more on the tail. The ventral surface is yellowish between the black bands. It is usually found on coral atolls and rocky islets where it congregates in large numbers during the breeding season. The eggs, laid in clutches of 5–9, hatch during June to August and the hatchlings resemble adults. Its prey includes moray eels. This handsome krait is occasionally found along the west coast of Thailand but is more common in West Malaysia and Singapore; it also occurs in the Bay of Bengal, the Indo-Australian Archipelago and the western Pacific. **Venomous and dangerous**. The BLACK-BANDED SEA KRAIT (*L. laticaudata*) is much rarer. It is very similar to the Yellow-lipped Sea Krait but can be recognized by the black labials and the curved yellow mark on the crown which may extend to the snout and around the eye to the labials. Its distribution is similar to that of the Yellow-lipped Sea Krait.

SEA SNAKES (Family Hydrophiidae)

These snakes are totally aquatic and normally marine, although by following rivers some venture several kilometres inland. Most are found a short distance offshore, different species preferring different aquatic habitats. The head shields are usually large, the ventral shields usually small and barely distinguishable from the body scales. They are well adapted to aquatic life: the nostrils are located near the top of the head and can be closed by a valve when the snake is submerged. The tail is greatly compressed and paddle-shaped to facilitate swimming. All species give birth to live young at sea and most prey primarily on eels and other fish; some specialize on fish eggs.

Banded Sea Snake *Hydrophis fasciatus* to 110cm

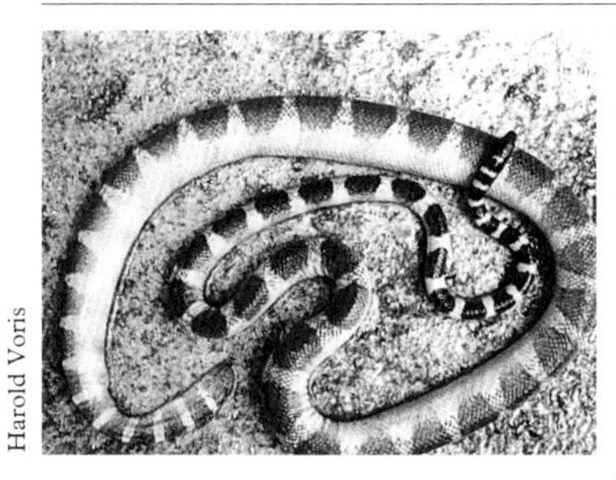

Harold Voris

The numerous species of the genus *Hydrophis* vary considerably in form and structure. All, however, are characterized by small ventrals, enlarged regular head shields, large anterior chin shields and a triangular mental. About 15 species inhabit the coastal waters around Thailand, Peninsular Malaysia and Singapore. Some *Hydrophis* species are bulky, but the Banded Sea Snake is one of the species with a very small head and slender anterior body. Nocturnal, it hunts mainly eels. Litters of 2–4 young are known. It occurs in shallow water along many eastern tropical Asian coasts. All *Hydrophis* species are **venomous and dangerous.**

Peron's, or Horned, Sea Snake *Acalyptophis peronii* to 140cm

Harold Voris

The spines above the large eyes distinguish this snake from all others. The scales of the stout body have a short keel and the ventrals are distinct. The head is pale brown or grey, the body greyish or pale brown above and whitish below, with 21–41 dark dorsal bars tapering to a point on the flanks, and three or four on the tail. The dark bars become obscure with age. This snake inhabits water to a depth of 50m, often near reefs. Rare in the Gulf of Thailand and South China Sea; more common in tropical Australian and western Pacific waters. **Venomous and dangerous**.

Beaked Sea Snake *Enhydrina schistosa* to 158cm

Ashok Captain

This snake receives its name from the rostral, which projects downwards past the supralabials. The head is distinct. The anterior portion of the body is thick, the posterior extremely thick. The skin appears loose, the scales have short keels, and the ventrals are distinct. Juveniles are grey or bluish-grey dorsally, whitish ventrally, with 43–49 dark rings which usually fade with maturity. The tail is dark. Most often found in shallow, muddy coastal waters, it sometimes ascends estuaries and rivers. Litters contain 2–33 young which are born from February through to May. It inhabits Indo-Pacific waters including both coasts of Thailand, Peninsular Malaysia, and Singapore. **Venomous and dangerous**.

Yellow-bellied Sea Snake *Pelamis platurus* to 90cm

Jennifer Daltry

The distinctive black and yellow coloration and lack of banding distinguish this species. Patterns are highly variable; most are yellow and black, some have brown coloration as well. The snout is long, the body greatly compressed. While occasionally found near shore, it appears to be most common in the open sea, where it is often found under or near floating debris where its food, pelagic fish, congregates. Litters of 2–6 neonates are born in spring. It has the most extensive range of any sea snake, occurring throughout the warm waters of the Indian and Pacific Oceans, including the waters off Thailand, West Malaysia, and Singapore. **Venomous and dangerous**.

COLUBRID SNAKES (Family Colubridae)

This family serves as a repository for snakes that do not clearly belong in other families. Therefore, it has both more species and more diverse species than any other family. Most are non-venomous, but a few are sufficiently venomous to be a threat to man. All have solid teeth; none has hollow fangs located on the anterior portion of the upper jaw, but some have enlarged, solid teeth on the posterior portion of the jaw – these species are described as 'rear fanged'. With about 130 species, Colubrids form the largest group of snakes in our area.

Reed Snakes (Subfamily Calamariinae)

These are small, burrowing snakes. The head is scarcely or not distinct from the neck. The eyes are moderate, with round pupils. The cylindrical body has smooth scales and a short tail. Twelve species of five genera occur in the area.

Variable Reed Snake *Calamaria lumbricoidea* to 64cm

Ulrich Manthey

The head is not distinct, but the shields are large. The ventrals are distinct and the tail is thick, tapering abruptly near the tip to form a sharp point. The body is dark brown or black above, with or without narrow, light stripes. The first one or two scale rows on the flank bordering the ventral shields are yellow, while the venter is yellow with or without black crossbands. The Variable Reed Snake is nocturnal and terrestrial and can be found under surface debris in lowland and hilly areas up to 1,400m. Its prey includes frogs, earthworms and other invertebrates which inhabit the soil. This handsome snake is found in southern Thailand, Peninsular and East Malaysia, Singapore, Indonesia east to Sulawesi, and the Philippines.

Malayan Mountain Reed Snake
Macrocalamus lateralis to 40cm

Gernot Vogel

The head is small, the body proportionally short. Usually uniformly reddish-brown above, but occasionally there are distinct yellow chevrons on the nape and head. There is a thin pale line on the lowest dorsal scales, but no stripes on the sides of the body. The ventral surface is yellow, orange or bright coral red. This poorly known mountain snake is found at 1,500–2,000m, under logs and other damp forest litter or basking in the sun. It preys on insects and their larvae. A clutch of 4 eggs is known. It is rare and only known to occur in the highlands of Perak and Pahang in Peninsular Malaysia.

Tweedie's Mountain Reed Snake
Macrocalamus tweediei to 50cm

Gernot Vogel

The body of this rare snake is uniform black with no lines or stripes, but the ventral surface shows a black and yellow chequered pattern, and the lower surface of the tail has a median black line which may be ill-defined. The ventral scales of young specimens are yellow with black edges. This rare snake has been found between 1,640m and 1,967m in damp environments under forest litter. Prey is reported to include house geckos (*Hemidactylus* species). This mountain reed snake is restricted to Peninsular Malaysia.

Rear-fanged Water Snakes
(Subfamily Homalopsinae)

The last two or three teeth on the rear of the upper jaw are grooved and often enlarged. The nostril is on the upper surface of the snout. The eyes are small and directed slightly upward. The head shields are large but sometimes fragmented. These are aquatic snakes, but are often found on land near water. Fish and frogs are their main prey. Fifteen species belonging to eight genera occur in the area.

Tentacled Snake *Erpeton tentaculatum* to 70cm

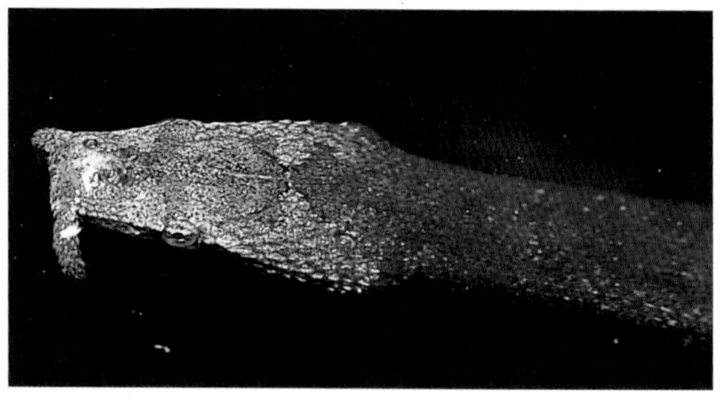

This unique snake has a pair of tentacle-like appendages extending from the rostral and used for luring fish. The head is distinct, the body scales strongly keeled and the ventrals very narrow. The colour and pattern are variable; markings in shades of brown are most common. The ventral surface is brownish-yellow. These docile animals are exclusively aquatic and inhabit still, acidic, freshwater bodies. They wait motionless for small fish, shrimps and other small prey to approach. There are 5–13 young per litter; they measure 20–24cm and resemble adults. The southern central plain and peninsular Thailand, as well as Cambodia and Vietnam, are home to these fascinating snakes.

Dog-faced Water Snake *Cerberus rynchops* to 120cm

The head of this snake is slightly distinct; its shields are large and sometimes fragmented. The small eyes, with vertically elliptical pupils, are located rather close to the snout. The stout body is cylindrical, the scales keeled, the ventrals smooth. The body is greyish, brownish or olivaceous above, with more or less distinct dark spots or crossbars. A black streak passes through the eye to the neck. The belly is either yellowish and heavily mottled with black or almost entirely dark grey. This snake inhabits mangroves, brackish river mouths and occasionally fresh water far inland. It feeds on fish. The young, born in litters of 8–26, measure 17–25cm and resemble adults. It occurs in the coastal areas of most of tropical Asia.

Crab-eating Water Snake or **Whitebelly Mangrove Snake** *Fordonia leucobalia* to 94cm

Mark O'Shea

The head is rounded and indistinct and the lower jaw is deeply countersunk. The stout cylindrical body bears smooth scales. These variable snakes may be grey, brown or purplish-black, with or without dark spots which pass on to the yellowish-white belly. The young have scattered dark spots. This nocturnal snake inhab its tidal rivers and coastal areas. It preys on small fish and crabs. Litters of 6–15 young, each 18cm long, are known. It occurs from southern Thailand through Malaysia and Singapore to Australia.

Bocourt's Water Snake *Enhydris bocourti* to 115cm

Piboon Jintakune

This is the largest member of genus *Enhydris* found in our area. The head is distinct, the pupil vertically elliptical. The body is stout and cylindrical, its scales smooth. The body colour is dark brown above with narrow, irregular, yellow crossbars. The lower sides are yellow with the dark dorsal colour sometimes extending across the belly. The head is dark with yellow marks above and yellow below. This nocturnal snake is found in well-watered lowlands. Females give birth to 6–17 young of about 22cm, each resembling an adult. It inhabits the coastal and lowland areas of Thailand and northern Peninsular Malaysia, as well as Cambodia and Vietnam.

Rainbow Water Snake *Enhydris enhydris* to 86cm

The head of this colourful snake is barely distinct. The cylindrical body has smooth scales. Its colour is grey or olive above with a light-brown stripe astride the vertebral ridge and pale stripes separated by thin black lines on each side. The head is brown with a pair of light-coloured lines converging on the snout. The belly is white or yellow with a dark median line or row of dots. This gentle snake is diurnal and found in lowland freshwater bodies, feeding mainly on fish. The young, 14cm replicas of adults, are born in litters of 4–18. It inhabits most of the Southeast Asian tropics, including Thailand south of 17°N, Peninsular Malaysia and Singapore.

Striped Water Snake *Enhydris jagorii* to 70cm

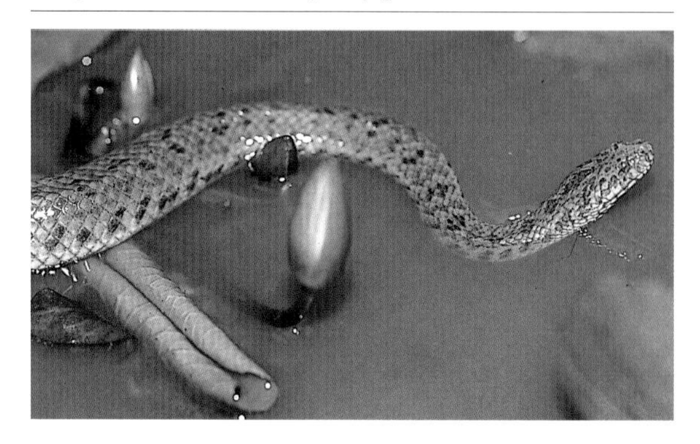

This rather small snake is greyish or olivaceous above with a characteristic series of blackish spots, usually arranged in pairs, on the vertebral line and larger angular spots on the sides. The ventrals and outer three or four scale rows are yellow, pink, or whitish; the outer margins of the ventrals and adjacent scale rows are heavily edged with grey. The head is grey above and slightly distinct. The body is oval, increasing in size posteriorly; its scales are smooth. This diurnal snake inhabits lowland freshwater streams, canals and lakes. It is found in much of Thailand, as far south as 8°N, and Indo-China.

Plumbeous, or **Yellowbelly, Water Snake**
Enhydris plumbea to 56cm

The body colour of this distinctive snake is greyish-olive or slaty grey above and changes abruptly to yellow low on the flanks. The ventral surface is dull white or pale yellow with black dots medially; the subcaudals have a median black line. The snout is broadly rounded and the head of this handsome snake is indistinct. The body is cylindrical to oval, short and stout, with smooth scales. This snake is found near fresh water, up to 1,200m. It is active by day and night and feeds on fish and frogs. Litters comprise 6–30 young, each 8–13cm long and with the adult coloration. It is widespread throughout Southeast Asia.

Puff-faced Water Snake *Homalopsis buccata* to 137cm

This common water snake is immediately identified by the large broad head. The stout body is cylindrical, with keeled scales. There is a white, mask-like pattern on the top of the head. The body is reddish-brown with many black-edged, yellowish cross-bars, but fades to uniform grey-brown in old animals. The belly is white with small black dots. Juveniles are black with white bands. Nocturnal and semi-aquatic, it inhabits the edges of freshwater rivers, ponds, canals and swamps up to 550m. It consumes fish and frogs. Females give birth to 2–20 young of about 23cm in a litter. This snake inhabits most of Southeast Asia, including Thailand south of 17°N, Malaysia and Singapore.

Gerard's Water Snake *Gerarda prevostiana* to 53cm

Indraneil Das

The body of this inconspicuous snake is proportionally long, the body scales are smooth, and the broad ventrals are not keeled. The head is slightly distinct from the neck, and bears large shields; the nostrils are dorsal and the eyes are small with vertically elliptical pupils. The snake is uniform grey or brown above; the belly is light brown with a median dark streak. The supralabials, chin and lowest three rows of flank scales are white. It inhabits coastal and tidal areas, including mangroves and estuaries, and it feeds mainly on fish and shrimp. It occurs in coastal areas of the Indian Ocean from Bombay to the west coast of Peninsular Malaysia, while there is an apparently isolated population in Chon Buri Province in southeast Thailand.

Natricine Snakes (Subfamily Natricinae)

This subfamily is diverse and poorly defined. The head and body characteristics are rather uniform, but dentition is very variable. Some species possess rear fangs and deaths have occurred from their bite, whereas others lack such fangs and are harmless. Most species have strongly keeled body scales and are referred to as keelbacks. Nine genera and 26 species of Natricine snake occur in our area.

Chequered Keelback *Xenochrophis piscator* to 110cm

Wolfgang Wüster

Wolfgang Wüster

(Above) Flavipunctatus *pattern;* (right) *juvenile*

This active snake bites fiercely but harmlessly. The distinct head has large eyes with round pupils. The body scales are keeled. The head is brown with black stripes extending from the eye and from behind the head to the supralabials. The stout body is olive-brown, rarely reddish, with dark spots arranged in alternating rows, creating a chequered appearance. The pattern is more distinct anteriorly than posteriorly. Hatchlings resemble adults. Adult animals with distinct head markings and black edges to all ventral and subcaudal scales have on occasion been thought to represent a separate species, *Xenochrophis flavipunctatus*, rather than individual colour variation. Active both day and night, this common terrestrial snake inhabits ponds, streams, flooded rice fields and other freshwater bodies up to 1,600m. Its prey includes fish and mice. This species is prolific: clutches containing 100 eggs have been recorded, although the normal range is 17–52. Incubation takes five to seven weeks, hatchlings measure 15–21cm. It occurs throughout sub-Himalayan Asia.

Triangle Keelback *Xenochrophis trianguligera* to 120cm

Piboon Jintakune

This Keelback has a slender olive-brown body with dark mottling. The sides are orange-red anteriorly, yellowish further back, with regularly spaced large triangular or oblong black blotches pointing downward and with a light spot in the upper part. The distinct head is olive above, the supralabials yellowish, narrowly edged with black. Juveniles resemble adults. The body scales are strongly keeled. Prey includes rodents, birds and frogs. Females lay several clutches of 5–8 eggs per year. This is a lowland, semi-aquatic snake, but has been recorded up to 1,400m in forests in southern Thailand, Malaysia, Singapore, Tenasserim and Indonesia.

Malayan Mountain Keelback *Amphiesma inas* to 90cm

Gernot Vogel

A small, slender, olive-brown snake. A series of light spots located anteriorly on each flank tends to merge into a line that continues to the posterior portion of the body. The head is brown with small dark spots, and the supralabials are light with dark markings. Dark-edged postocular light stripes, sometimes broken into light spots, join the dorsolateral stripes on the body. The ventral surface is light yellow but each ventral scale has a black edge. The body scales are keeled, the ventrals are rounded. It occurs at higher elevations in northeastern and peninsular Thailand, and in Peninsular Malaysia.

Modest Keelback *Amphiesma modesta* to 72cm

Ashok Captain

The head of this attractive snake is distinct, and the eyes are moderate with round pupils. The nostrils are on the sides of the snout. The slender body is cylindrical and the scales are feebly keeled. The body is brown above with small black spots and small yellow spots on the sides which may form a stripe. A yellow stripe extends from behind the eye to the neck. The labials have black edges. The ventrals are almost entirely black on Thai snakes. This terrestrial forest snake preys on frogs and is found at 700–900m. It is uncommon but occurs in northern Thailand, ranging to Cambodia, southern China and Assam.

Striped Keelback *Amphiesma stolata* to 73cm

Wolfgang Wüster

This is a fairly common snake whose greenish-brown head is distinct while its cylindrical body bears strongly keeled scales. Two yellow or buff stripes extend along the sides of the olive-green or brownish body and tail, sometimes with small black spots anteriorly. It inhabits well-watered plains and hills up to 2,000m. Diurnal and predominantly terrestrial, it hunts frogs and toads. Females produce 3–12 eggs per clutch. Hatchlings are 13–17cm long and resemble adults. This snake occurs in most of Thailand north of 12°N and adjoining areas.

ASIAN KEELBACKS (Genus *Rhabdophis*)

The *Rhabdophis* keelbacks have enlarged rear fangs to deliver mild venom to their prey. Human fatalities have involved *Rhabdophis* species found outside our area, but not those within it. Nevertheless, all members should be considered **dangerous**.

Speckle-bellied Keelback *Rhabdophis chrysargus* to 77cm

Wolfgang Grossmann

The head of this attractive snake is dark brown or black. The supralabials are white with black sutures; the chin and throat are plain white. The greenish-brown, slender, cylindrical body bears small red flank spots which fade posteriorly. The venter is white with black spots on the lateral margins. Juveniles have a white chevron on the neck. This species inhabits montane forests up to 1,700m, where it is most often found along streams during daytime. It preys on mice, small birds, frogs and lizards. Clutches of 3–10 eggs hatch after 7–9 weeks to produce hatchlings of 15–22cm. It occurs throughout mainland Southeast Asia, Hainan, the Philippines and much of Indonesia.

Green Keelback *Rhabdophis nigrocinctus* to 95cm

Henrik Bringsøe

Gernot Vogel

Juvenile

The body of this handsome snake is dark green but becomes brownish-green posteriorly. Each side of the body has black bars which may join on the vertebral ridge. The head is dark brown with black lines; the supralabials are grey. The chin, throat, and ventrals are white, becoming greyish posteriorly, the subcaudals are dark grey with white edges. This nocturnal snake preys on frogs and fish. It occurs up to 2,100m in Thailand, south to Surat Thani, as well as in Myanmar, Indo-China and Yunnan.

Red-necked Keelback *Rhabdophis subminiatus* to 130cm

Wolfgang Wüster

Juvenile

The head of this attractive snake is olive, the neck reddish. Not all specimens bear a black line from the eye to the supralabials. The body is uniformly olive-green, the venter grey. Hatchlings are especially brightly coloured. This diurnal snake prefers well watered forested lowlands and hills up to 1,780m. It preys on mainly frogs and toads. Clutches of 5–17 eggs hatch after 8–10 weeks; the young are 13–19cm. It occurs throughout Thailand and northern peninsular Malaysia, ranging to Sikkim, Hainan and western Indonesia. This uneven-tempered snake should be considered **dangerous**; human bite victims have suffered severe symptoms, but no fatalities have been reported.

Blue-necked Keelback *Macropisthodon rhodomelas* to 52cm

Lim Boo Liat

This attractive snake rears up and flattens its neck like a cobra when disturbed. The head is distinct from the neck; the eye is moderate, the pupil round. The body is rather stout, with strongly keeled scales and rounded ventrals. The head is light olive-green. The wide, black chevron on the neck continues as a black line over the spine. The sides of the neck are soft blue; the flanks are pinkish-brown crossed by faint thin lines extending from the vertebral stripe. The belly is pink or yellow with small black dots near the edge of each ventral. This terrestrial and semi-aquatic snake has been found in forests, plantations and damp meadows up to 210m and may be active at any time. A clutch of 25 eggs is known. It occurs in southern Thailand, Malaysia, Singapore and parts of Indonesia.

Boonsong's Mountain Keelback
Opisthotropis boonsongi to 100cm

Tanya Chan-ard

This rare snake is large for the genus *Opisthotropis*. Its snout is broadly rounded and its head is distinct. The eyes are rather large, the pupils round. The body is cylindrical, stout, and covered with keeled scales. The body and top of the head are light brown, becoming lighter on the flanks. The ventral surface is either creamy white or brown mottled; the supralabials, chin and throat are cream. The three specimens caught to date were found at night in mountain streams at approximately 700m. Nothing is known of its diet. Boonsong's Mountain Keelback has been recorded only in northeastern Thailand.

Assamese Mountain Snake *Plagiopholis nuchalis* to 52cm

Tanya Chan-ard

The body of this attractive little snake is reddish-brown. Because many scales have black edges it appears to have a banded pattern. The head is dark brown and there is a distinct, dark chevron on the neck, its apex pointing toward the head. There are two dark marks below the eye. The head is not distinct; the eyes are moderate and the pupils vertically sub-elliptic. The body is cylindrical and bears scales that are either smooth or keeled posteriorly. A terrestrial mountain species, it has been recorded at 655–1,300m. Its diet consists primarily of earthworms. It inhabits western, northern and northeastern Thailand, and Assam, Myanmar and Yunnan.

Common Mock Viper *Psammodynastes pulverulentus* to 44cm

(Below)
Neonates

Wolfgang Grossmann

The head is distinctly triangular, and as a result the Common Mock Viper is often confused with venomous vipers; it is harmless. A ridge extends from the eye to the snout, the eyes are large, and the pupils are vertical. The body is cylindrical, its scales smooth. The base colour is brown or reddish, ventrally light brown or pink; the pattern is quite variable. This terrestrial species inhabits hill and montane forests above 700m, but occasionally much lower. Its prey includes lizards and frogs, which it hunts during both night and day. The 5–10 live young in a litter are 15–18cm replicas of adults. It occurs throughout Southeast Asia to Nepal, Taiwan and the Philippines.

Big-eyed Mountain Keelback or **Big-eyed Bamboo Snake**
Pseudoxenodon macrops to 120cm

Anita Malhotra

When threatened, this harmless snake rears its head and neck, and flattens its neck to mimic a cobra. The head is distinct; the eyes are large with round pupils. The cylindrical body has keeled scales. There is a black chevron on the neck, its apex pointed toward the head. The head and body are brown to grey. There are yellowish or reddish spots along the vertebral ridge and black spots on the sides. The Big-eyed Mountain Keelback is a snake most often found in forest near streams at altitudes between 150 and 2,000m. Frogs are known prey. A clutch of 10 eggs is known. It ranges from Nepal and southern China, through northern and northeastern Thailand, to the Cameron Highlands in Peninsular Malaysia.

Colubrine Snakes (Subfamily Colubrinae)

This subfamily includes a number of snakes whose nostrils are usually located on the sides of the head; the head is covered with large shields and the ventrals are well developed. Some are primarily terrestrial, others are arboreal. Some have solid teeth throughout; in others the last two or three posterior teeth on the upper jaw are grooved. About 80 species of 21 genera have been reported to inhabit Thailand, Peninsular Malaysia and Singapore.

RACERS or RAT SNAKES (Genus *Elaphe*)

The teeth on the upper jaw may be slightly enlarged. The head is rather distinct from the neck, and the pupil is round. These are oviparous, terrestrial snakes, although they are good climbers. They prey on mammals and birds.

Yunnan Stripe-tailed Rat Snake
Elaphe taeniura yunnanensis to 180cm

Jarujin Nabhitabhata

The slender head of this colourful snake is brown with a black streak extending back from the eye. There are two dorsal rows of black blotches and two rows on the sides, which merge into brown or black stripes on the posterior third of the body. The ventral surface is yellow to yellowish-grey. The dorsal scales are smooth or slightly keeled, and the ventrals have well-developed keels. Active both day and night, this snake is found at 700–3,100m. It is found in eastern Thailand and adjacent regions.

Cave Dwelling Snake *Elaphe taeniura ridleyi* to 250cm

Wolfgang Grossmann

The anterior two-thirds of the body of this handsome snake are greenish-yellow to beige, occasionally with a light yellow vertebral stripe. The last third of the body has a yellow vertebral stripe with a black stripe on each side. The top of the head is grey-blue, the snout light brown or orange. A black line extends from the eyes to the corner of the mouth. The belly is white. The dorsal scales are smooth anteriorly, strongly keeled posteriorly. Active by day and night, this snake lives in or near limestone caves and preys primarily on bats. Clutches comprise 7–15 eggs, hatchlings are 30–35cm long. It inhabits southern Thailand and northern Peninsular Malaysia.

Common Malayan Racer or **Black Copper Rat Snake**
Elaphe flavolineata to 180cm

Merel J. Cox

The pattern varies but usually the body is dark brown or blackish with distinct black blotches on the anterior. There is also a black stripe on each anterior side of the bright yellowish-orange vertebral column. The head is dark above, with several black stripes extending below and behind each eye along the lower part of the neck. The body is cylindrical, the scales smooth or feebly keeled, the vertebrals slightly enlarged. The ventral keels are well developed. This diurnal snake lays clutches of 5–12 eggs; 25–30cm hatchlings emerge after about 15 weeks. This snake is found up to 900m from Thailand south of 14°N to Borneo and Java.

Copperhead Racer or **Radiated Rat Snake**
Elaphe radiata to 230cm

Merel J. Cox

The body of this rather common snake is compressed. The vertebral dorsal scales are weakly keeled but not enlarged. The body is greyish or yellowish-brown with four black stripes on the anterior part of the body. The head is coppery brown with three black streaks radiating from the eye; one extends back to the narrow black band over the nape. This active diurnal snake inhabits open country up to 1,480m. Females produce several clutches of about 5–12 eggs per year, hatchlings are 25–30cm long. When cornered it expands its throat longitudinally, throws the anterior part of its body into loops, opens its mouth, and strikes repeatedly. It is found throughout Southeast Asia and the eastern Himalayas.

Red Mountain Racer *Elaphe porphyracea porphyracea* to 120cm

Jarujin Nabhitabhata

This stunningly beautiful snake is slender with the head being only slightly distinct from the neck. Dorsal scales may be smooth or weakly keeled, the ventrals are not keeled. Adults are deep brick-red with 14–16 black crossbars on the body and three or four on the tail. In the young the areas separated by the crossbars are alternately red and yellow. Active at dawn and dusk, this snake inhabits forests between 1,000–2,600m. Clutches of 3–7 eggs produce hatchlings of 25–30cm. It occurs in the Himalayan foothills including northern Thailand and possibly Peninsular Malaysia

Black-striped Mountain Racer
Elaphe porphyracea nigrofasciata to 96cm

Klaus-Dieter Schulz

In body proportions and scale characters this handsome snake resembles the typical form, but it differs greatly in coloration. The body is reddish-brown, with narrow black stripes extending from the eye to the tail tip, flanking the vertebral ridge. There may be crossbars creating alternately red and yellow spaces. The ventral surface is light in colour. This racer inhabits humid forests above 800m and is active at dusk. Clutches of 2 or 3 eggs yield hatchlings of about 30cm. In Thailand, it has been found only in the north east.

Green Tree Racer *Elaphe prasina* to 120cm

Andreas Gümprecht

This attractive snake is uniformly bright green without any markings. The belly is pale green, and the ends of the ventral shields are white or yellow outside the lateral keel. The tongue is reddish-brown. The eyes are large and the iris yellowish. The body scales are faintly keeled except for the smooth, lowermost ones. Ventral keels are well developed. The Green Tree Racer is diurnal and is found near water in bamboo clumps or in forests at 500–1,640m. Clutches contain 5–8 eggs, hatchlings are 20–25cm long. It occurs in Peninsular Malaysia, northern Thailand and adjacent areas to the north.

Red-tailed Ratsnake *Gonyosoma oxycephalum* to 240cm

This swift snake differs from the Green Tree Racer in many details. The head and body are green, the tail rusty brown or red. The belly is light green or greenish-yellow. A sharply defined line, running through the large eye, separates the darker green of the crown from the lighter lower part. The snout projects strongly. The body is strongly compressed with smooth or faintly keeled scales. Arboreal and diurnal, it inhabits forest up to 1,100m and preys on rodents, birds and bats. Clutches of 5–12 eggs are laid; hatchlings measure 40–55cm and resemble adults. The blue tongue is flicked and moved very slowly. This snake occurs throughout Southeast Asia.

Indo-Chinese Rat Snake *Ptyas korros* to 256cm

Jarujin Nabhitabhata

The anterior half of the body of this common snake is olive, the remainder brown with dark-edged scales. The grey-brown head is elongate, distinct from the neck, the very large eyes contain round pupils. The body scales are smooth or feebly keeled on the posterior part of the body. Juveniles have transverse rows of white spots across the anterior part of the body. Diurnal, it inhabits forests and agricultural land up to 3,000m. It preys on a wide range of small animals, including rodents and frogs. Females lay 4–12 eggs per clutch, hatchlings measure 36–38cm. Frequently seen throughout Thailand, Malaysia and Singapore, it ranges to Assam, Taiwan and Bali.

Common Rat Snake *Ptyas mucosus* to 320cm

Wolfgang Wüster

This large snake has a brown head, while the body colour is pale to medium brown. Posteriorly there are black transverse bands across the back and down the sides to the ventrals. The head is distinct, and the large eye has a round pupil. The scales are smooth; the vertebrals may be slightly enlarged. Juveniles resemble adults. This terrestrial snake is found in various habitats up to 1,000m. It is a good climber and preys on a wide range of animals. Clutches of 6–18 eggs yield hatchlings 37–47cm long. This snake is widely distributed in sub-Himalayan Asia, from Iran to Taiwan and to Java.

Keeled Rat Snake *Ptyas carinatus* to 375cm

Gernot Vogel

The body of this large snake is olive-brown to nearly black anteriorly, sometimes with indistinct yellow crossbars, while posteriorly it is yellowish with a bold black chequered or reticulate pattern. The tail is black with yellow spots. The head is brown above, white below, and distinct from the neck. The large eyes have round pupils. The triangular body bears smooth or keeled scales. This diurnal, terrestrial snake is a good climber and is found up to 1,500m. It preys on anything it can catch. About 10 eggs form a clutch. Easily confused with the King Cobra, it is found localized in Southeast Asia, including parts of Thailand, Malaysia and Singapore.

White-bellied Rat Snake *Ptyas fuscus* to 290cm

This attractive snake is brown above, sometimes with a red vertebral stripe. The posterior part of the body and tail has a black lateral stripe that progressively broadens so that the tail may be wholly black above. The sharp line of demarcation between this black stripe and the yellowish-white belly is striking. The head is long and distinct, its shields large. The large eyes have round pupils. The body is slightly compressed, its scales are smooth. This active snake is found up to 914m. It is terrestrial and preys on rats and lizards. This rare snake occurs in southern Thailand, Peninsular Malaysia, Singapore, Sumatra, Borneo, and nearby islands.

Malayan Ringneck *Liopeltis tricolor* to 56cm

Ulrich Manthey

This poorly known snake is greenish or olive above and yellow below. It has a conspicuous black streak on each side of the head, which passes through the eye and extends to the anterior part of the body, tapering and dying out a few centimetres behind the head. The head is flattened, the long snout precedes the moderate eye; pupils are round. Body is cylindrical, covered with smooth scales. A terrestrial forest snake which often hides among leaf litter, it has been found up to 1,200m. The Malayan Ringneck occurs in Malaysia, Singapore, Brunei, Indonesia east to Java and the southern Philippines.

Indo-Chinese Sand Snake
Psammophis condanarus indochinensis to 110cm

Piboon Jintakune

The head of this handsome snake is distinct. A ridge extends from the eye to the snout, the eyes are large and the pupils round. The cylindrical body has smooth, shiny scales. The body is pale olive or buff with four dark-brown, black-edged longitudinal stripes. The head is brown with distinct longitudinal markings. The Indo-Chinese Sand Snake is terrestrial but a good climber. It prefers forests up to 1,967m, where it preys on lizards, frogs and small rodents. Swelling may result from the bite of this mild-mannered snake, but it is not considered dangerous. It inhabits the central plain, north, and northeast regions of Thailand and Myanmar.

Common Blackhead or **Collared Many-toothed Snake**

Sibynophis collaris to 85cm

Gernot Vogel

The head of this attractive little snake is dark olive to brown, usually with small, darker markings. The pattern on the neck varies, but in our area it is a triangular collar bordered by yellowish-white. The body is brown to grey-brown, with a black stripe or row of black dots down the vertebral ridge. The Common Blackhead occurs at moderate and high elevations in forest undergrowth. Its food consists primarily of skinks. Females lay clutches of up to 6 eggs. It inhabits most of Thailand and Peninsular Malaysia, as well as the eastern Himalayan foothills.

Malayan Many-toothed Snake

Sibynophis melanocephalus to 80cm

The head is reddish to dark brown anteriorly, black posteriorly; the neck is pale orange. The body is grey-brown to brown with a black stripe on the vertebral ridge flanked by light-yellow to brown stripes that contain dark spots or bars. The entire pattern gradually becomes obscure toward the tail. Like other *Sibynophis* species, it has a relatively distinct head, a cylindrical body covered with smooth scales, a very long tail, and round pupils. Diurnal and terrestrial, this snake is usually found near streams in rainforest up to 1,100m. Skinks, frogs, tadpoles and grasshoppers feature in its diet. It occurs in southern Thailand, Malaysia, Singapore and Indonesia east to Java.

KUKRI SNAKES (Genus *Oligodon*)

Kukri snakes have short, indistinct heads and cylindrical, often stout bodies covered with smooth scales. The rostral shield is very large, the pupil is round. Many species have a distinct chevron mark on the nape. Colour and pattern of some species are highly variable, making identification difficult. Kukri snakes are terrestrial and mainly nocturnal; all are oviparous. The teeth are modified to cut open both bird and reptile eggs, a favourite food of members of this genus. Smaller members prey on insects, grubs and spiders, while larger species eat small rodents, lizards, birds and frogs. Kukri snake species are variable in temper and while none is known to be venomous, the slashing teeth can impart cuts that heal very slowly.

Barron's Kukri Snake *Oligodon barroni* to 45cm

Jennifer Daltry

The head and body of this attractive little snake are light brown with 10–12 dark brown bars on the body and tail, often parallel to small spots. A dark-brown stripe passes from the top of the head, through the eye, to the fifth supralabial; another stripe extends from the head to the third ventral, and there is a heart-shaped spot on the neck. The venter is pink to coral with two rows of brown quadrangular marks extending on to the subcaudals. Barron's Kukri Snake prefers plains and hills up to 300m. It inhabits only the southeastern provinces of Thailand, as well as Cambodia and southern Vietnam.

Grey Kukri Snake *Oligodon joynsoni* to 81cm

Suthigit Patramangorn

The stout body of this relatively rare snake is tan or brown with either a reticulated pattern or a black-barred pattern; the black pigment is confined to scale edges and the pattern may be vague. A narrow, broken, yellowish vertebral stripe may be present. The head is tan or brown with part or all of the usual chevron pattern. The venter and subcaudals are white or yellow, either unmarked or with randomly arranged brown or black spots which may become dominant posteriorly. The body scales are arranged in 17 rows. This snake has been found in forested areas at moderate to high altitude in northern and western Thailand, Laos and Vietnam.

Brown Kukri Snake *Oligodon purpurascens* to 89cm

Jarujin Nabhitabhata

This rarely seen snake has a purplish-brown body with a series of dark-edged blotches, irregularly spaced, across its back and extending to the tail. The blotches extend down the sides of the body; some posterior ones nearly reach the ventrals. Narrow indistinct reticulations are often present between the blotches. Ventrally immaculate pink or yellow anteriorly, dark pigmentation progressively intrudes onto the ventrals, dominating the posterior ventrals and anterior subcaudals, then recedes so that the posterior subcaudals are nearly immaculate. This nocturnal, terrestrial, semi-fossorial snake prefers wooded country. Clutches of 8–13 eggs are known, hatchlings are 21cm long. It occurs in southern Thailand, Malaysia, Singapore, Borneo and Indonesia east to Java.

Banded Kukri Snake *Oligodon fasciolatus* to 115cm

The head and body of this variable snake are tan, brown or grey-brown, with three possible patterns: reticulated, in which a network formed by black-edged scales sometimes creates crossbars; black-barred, caused by black-edged scales; and blotched, in which the brown or dark brown pigment covers four to six scale rows and is bordered outside with black. Each pattern may have paired brown stripes flanking the vertebral ridge, and faint lateral stripes one scale wide. The belly and subcaudals are white or yellow. This snake is found in forests up to 700m. Clutches of 3–16 eggs are known. It occurs throughout Thailand to just north of the Malaysian border.

Cambodian Kukri Snake *Oligodon mouhoti* to 40cm

The body of this attractive little snake is brown or greyish with a light vertebral stripe bordered by two light-brown stripes extending along its flanks. A thin light-brown stripe extends along the fourth dorsal scale row. There are two distinct dark bands on the dorsal surface of the tail, one at the base, the other at the tip. The ventral surface is red with irregularly arranged, small, black bars on individual ventrals. A dark-brown stripe extends from the back of the eye to the ventrals. This snake mimics the coral snakes. It occurs in the forested lowlands and foothills of western, central and eastern Thailand through Cambodia and southern Vietnam.

Inornate Kukri Snake *Oligodon inornatus* to 64cm

Jarujin Nabhitabhata

The body of this rare snake is tan or brown, either patternless or with a reticulated pattern in which black pigment is confined to scale edges, sometimes forming crossbars. There may be a pair of faint grey stripes, two to three scales wide, flanking the vertebral area, and a similar, narrow stripe on each side. The head is grey or brown, either unmarked or with all or part of the traditional pattern. The belly is white or yellow, either uniform or with occasional brown markings; the subcaudals are unmarked white or yellow. There are 15 rows of body scales. The Inornate Kukri Snake occurs only in northeastern and southeastern Thailand and adjacent Cambodia.

Striped Kukri Snake *Oligodon taeniatus* to 44cm

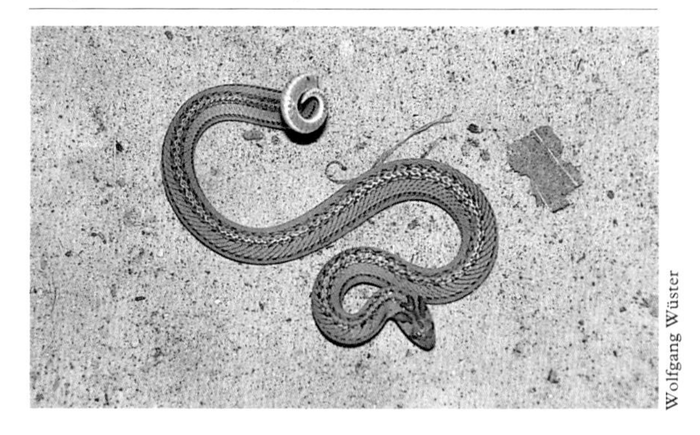

Wolfgang Wüster

This handsome little snake has a grey to brown body with two narrow, dark-brown stripes flanking the vertebral ridge. The vertebral ridge is light and has small yellow spots. There are no dark spots on the dorsal surface of the tail. A broad, dark-brown band extends from the snout, through the eyes, to the supralabials; another extends from the crown to the base of the jaw, but does not reach the ventral scales. The chin is white, the venter orangish-red with irregular, black, quadrangular markings, largest and most frequent near the vent. This species occurs localized over much of Thailand, Indo-China and Yunnan.

Gray's Kukri Snake *Oligodon dorsalis* to 55cm

Merel J. Cox

The head is dark brown and usually suggests two crossbars, one before and one behind the eye, as well as a chevron. The dark-brown to purplish body bears a light vertebral stripe which is either black-edged or contains small black spots. Another black stripe extends along the second and third dorsal scale rows. The dorsal surface of the tail usually has two or three large black spots. The belly is mostly black, the underside of the tail yellowish-orange. This snake inhabits dry, forested areas. Thai specimens have been found at 1,300m in the north east; the species also occurs in Myanmar, Bangladesh and northeastern India.

WOLF SNAKES (Genus *Lycodon*)

The head is slightly distinct. The eyes are moderate, with vertical pupils. These nocturnal, terrestrial snakes prey primarily on lizards. They are oviparous.

Common Wolf, or **House, Snake**
Lycodon capucinus (Lycodon aulicus) to 76cm

The head is somewhat flattened, the snout projects over the lower jaw, and the shields are large. The elongate, cylindrical body is brown or purplish-brown with fine, white or yellow reticulations. The top of the head is brown, and there is a light band at the back of the head. The labials are yellowish and the belly white. This snake inhabits dry forested areas but is sometimes found near cultivated areas. It preys on geckos, other lizards and frogs, and lays clutches of 3–11 eggs. The species occurs throughout Southeast Asia.

Scarce Wolf Snake *Lycodon effraenis* to 75cm

Wolfgang Grossmann

Juvenile

The pattern of the Scarce Wolf Snake changes with its age. Hatchlings are brown with a series of white or yellow rings completely encircling the body throughout its length. A white streak extends from the snout to behind the eyes; the supralabials are white. These bright markings gradually become mottled with brown and disappear at maturity. They remain only as sparse and irregular flecks of yellow on solid-brown adults. The slender, cylindrical body bears smooth scales. Although terrestrial, the Scarce Wolf Snake is a good climber. It inhabits lowland forests in southern Thailand, Malaysia, Singapore, Sumatra and Kalimantan.

Laotian, or **Indo-Chinese, Wolf Snake**
Lycodon laoensis to 56cm

Jarujin Nabhitabhata

The head and the anterior supralabials of this striking snake are deep blue; the posterior labials and the chin are cream. The black body is crossed by 13–29 yellow bands with 8–18 on the tail. The anterior bands are much wider than posterior ones, occasionally widening to enclose areas of black. The ventral surface is entirely white. This secretive snake hides under debris in shaded areas by day and hunts lizards and frogs at night. Females produce about 5 eggs per clutch. This species inhabits lowlands and hills throughout Thailand, in northern Peninsular Malaysia, Yunnan and Indo-China.

Malayan Banded Wolf Snake *Lycodon subcinctus* to 118cm

Jennifer Daltry

(Above) *Adult;* (below) *juvenile*

Wolfgang Wüster

Like the Scarce Wolf Snake, this snake changes pattern with age. Young specimens have up to 20 white bands but as they mature the bands gradually disappear, the posterior ones fading first. Adults are dark brown or black with widely spaced white bands anteriorly which progressively darken until the posterior part of the body is uniformly black. This snake resembles the venomous Malayan Krait, but it has feebly keeled scales, its vertebrals are not enlarged and the scales in its white bands do not have black edges. It inhabits well-drained areas up to 1,770m. Nocturnal and terrestrial, it probably feeds mostly on geckos and skinks. Females lay 5–11 eggs which hatch after 10–12 weeks; hatchlings are about 24cm long. It is distributed over most of Southeast Asia.

Slender Wolf Snake *Lepturophis borneensis* to 160cm

Wolfgang Grossmann

This long, slender snake is brown, dark grey or black dorsally, and white or cream ventrally. Its labials, chin, and throat are white. Juveniles have many broad whitish bands. The head is distinct and depressed, and the moderate-sized eyes have vertical pupils. This snake has strongly keeled body scales; the ventrals are keeled and notched laterally, indicating arboreal as well as terrestrial habits. The tail is very long and slender. It inhabits forests up to 1,100m, where it is most frequently found near streams. Little is known of its habits but it is nocturnal and known to eat frogs and lizards. It occurs in southern Thailand, Peninsular Malaysia, Sarawak and Sabah.

Common, or **Blanford's, Bridle Snake**
Dryocalamus davisonii to 92cm

Piboon Jintakune

The slender, smooth-scaled body of this colourful snake has 33–40 black crossbands astride the vertebral ridge and extending half-way down the sides; the tail has 27–32 black bands. The remainder of the body is white to greenish, as is the ventral surface. The snout is black, while the crown of the depressed head is heavily dusted with light pigment; the labials, chin, and throat are white. This snake prefers lowland forested areas up to 300m. It is a good climber which hunts lizards at night. Clutches contain 3 or 4 eggs. It occurs in Thailand south to Krabi, Myanmar and Indo-China.

Gernot Vogel

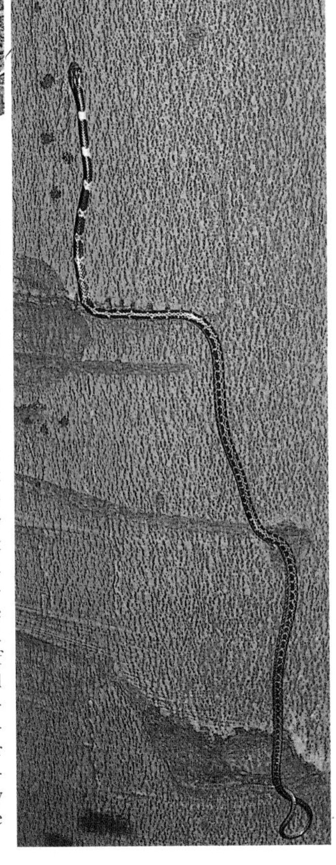

Gernot Vogel

(Above) *Striped form;* (right) *banded form*

This beautiful species occurs in two patterns. In both, the top of the head is brown with yellow pigment, which creates a masked appearance. One pattern consists of five yellow, rough-edged, parallel stripes: a single line begins behind the head and extends along the spine to the tail tip; a pair begins at each jaw and continues to the tail tip, while another pair extends along the first and second scale rows. In the second variety, chocolate-brown bands cross the vertebral ridge and extend half-way down the sides of the body. This arboreal and nocturnal snake inhabits plains and hills in southern Thailand, Peninsular and East Malaysia, Singapore, Sumatra and nearby islands, Borneo and the southern Philippines.

FLYING SNAKES (Genus *Chrysopelea*)

Three species of 'flying' snake reside in our area. They cannot fly, of course, but they can flatten their bodies and glide short distances from tree to tree. All have a rounded snout and a somewhat flattened head. The eyes are large and the pupils round. The body is elongated, slender and slightly compressed. The ventrals have a suture-like lateral keel and a notch on each side coinciding with the keel. The subcaudals are in two rows, keeled and notched like ventrals. These last two characteristics make members of this genus superb climbers. They are oviparous and eat a wide variety of prey.

Golden Tree Snake *Chrysopelea ornata* to 130cm

Peter Mudde

The head of this attractive snake is green with black markings; the chin and supralabials are ivory. The body is greenish-yellow. Each smooth body scale has a black edge; some scales are entirely black, forming crossbars. The ventrals are green with black spots next to each lateral notch. This diurnal snake inhabits plains and hills up to 550m and preys on lizards, rodents, and other snakes. Clutches of 6–12 eggs are known; hatchlings are 15–20cm long and resemble adults but their colour and pattern are brighter. This agile snake has been found in every region of Thailand and in northern Peninsular Malaysia, as well as in the Indian and south Chinese regions, Myanmar and Indo-China.

Twin-barred Tree Snake *Chrysopelea pelias* to 74cm

Raynoo Homhual Cox

This beautiful snake is very rare. The upper head is light brown and crossed by three black-edged orange bars. A narrow black line separates the crown from the white labials and chin. Most of the upper body is reddish-orange, crossed by black-edged white bars which do not reach the flanks. The light-brown sides are heavily speckled with small bluish-white blotches. The ventral surface is yellowish-white, and a thin black line extends along the edges of the ventral scales. The body scales may be slightly keeled. The ecology of this arboreal snake is poorly known. It inhabits southern Thailand, Malaysia, Singapore, Sumatra, Borneo and nearby islands.

Paradise Tree Snake *Chrysopelea paradisi* to 120cm

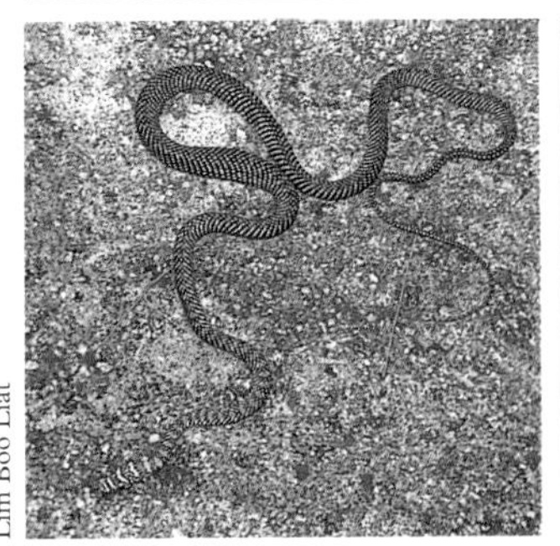

Lim Boo Liat

Gernot Vogel

Unfortunately, this beautiful snake is rare everywhere within its range. The head is black and crossed by five narrow, greenish-yellow bands. The bands become large, greenish-yellow blotches on the neck; occasionally their colour is reddish-orange. The blotches are succeeded by red or reddish-orange spots on the body, and smaller, light-green dots occur on the tail. The remaining body scales are black with a green spot in each centre, giving the sides of the body a speckled appearance. This diurnal and arboreal snake inhabits forests up to 1,500m. It eats geckos, frogs and bats. Clutches contain 5–8 eggs. It inhabits southern Thailand, Malaysia, Singapore, Indonesia and the Philippines.

Keel-bellied, or Red, Whip Snake
Dryophiops rubescens to 100cm

Wolfgang Wüster

The brown-patterned head of this slender snake is elongated and distinct with a ridge between the large eye and the snout. The pupils are horizontal. The slender body is compressed, the scales smooth. The ventrals and subcaudals are keeled and notched. The body is greyish or reddish-brown with a vertebral series of black spots. The belly is yellow anteriorly, progressively more heavily mottled with brown posteriorly, and with scattered black dots. This diurnal and exclusively arboreal snake prefers forests up to 500m and consumes frogs and geckos. A clutch of 2 eggs is known. It inhabits southern Thailand, Malaysia, Singapore, much of Indonesia and the southern Philippines.

WHIP SNAKES (Genus *Ahaetulla*)

Whip snakes are long, slender, arboreal snakes which prey primarily on lizards. The elongated head is distinct, and there is a prominent ridge between the eyes and the snout. The eyes are horizontally oval and contain horizontal pupils. The body is compressed, the scales smooth, the vertebral scales enlarged. These snakes give birth to living young. Four members of the genus inhabit our area.

Speckle-headed Whip Snake *Ahaetulla fasciolata* to 140cm

Gernot Vogel

The head pattern distinguishes this handsome snake: it is grey or brownish above, spotted or finely stippled with black curved lines and rings. The body is brownish or pinkish-grey dorsally, with numerous faint crossbars on the neck and anterior part of the body. The ventral surface is white, with a black line on the edges of each ventral and often a black median line. The snout is pointed. This snake has been found between 491m and 984m. Arboreal and diurnal, it feeds primarily upon cold-blooded prey. It occurs in Thailand, Malaysia, Singapore, Sumatra, and Borneo.

Malayan Green Whip Snake *Ahaetulla mycterizans* to 108cm

This is the least known of the region's whip snakes. The body coloration is green, sometimes brown or grey above, white and sometimes with a green median line below. The ventral colour usually agrees with the dorsal colour. A white line extends along the outer edge of the ventral scales throughout the length of the body. It is very similar to the Oriental Whip Snake, but differs in possessing a single anal shield and fewer ventral (186–195) and subcaudal (115–156) scales. This snake is arboreal, active during the day, and preys primarily on cold-blooded prey. It inhabits the forested foothills of southern Thailand and Peninsular Malaysia and also occurs on Java.

Long-nosed Whip Snake *Ahaetulla nasuta* to 127cm

Wolfgang Wüster

This snake is easily identified by the relatively long, pointed appendage protruding from the rostral. Coloration varies from tan to grey and yellow. However, it is most often dark green above and light green below. The tail is long. Diurnal and arboreal, it normally lives in forests and agricultural areas among bushes and trees but has also been found on roads. Its prey includes lizards and birds. Females give birth to 3–23 young; the newborn are about 30cm long at birth and are light yellow, light grey or pale green. This species occurs in Thailand north of the Isthmus of Kra, Indo-China, Myanmar and the Indian Subcontinent.

Oriental Whip Snake *Ahaetulla prasina* to 197cm

Jarujin Nabhitabhata

This is the largest and most common whip snake in our area, and frequently seen even in large cities. The body is usually pale to dark green above and pale green below with a thin white line along the edges of the ventrals, but coloration may vary from grey to orange and brown. It is similar to the Malayan Green Whip Snake, but its anal shield is divided and it has more ventrals (194–235) and subcaudals (151–235). This arboreal, diurnal snake preys mostly on lizards. Young are born in litters of 4–10; the newborn are about 35cm long and resemble adults. The Oriental Whip Snake inhabits forested areas up to 2,100m throughout Southeast Asia.

BRONZEBACKS (Genus *Dendrelaphis*)

Bronzebacks have a distinct head and large eyes with round pupils. The loreal area is concave. The body is slender, the scales smooth and the vertebral scales enlarged. The tail is long. The ventrals have a notch and a lateral keel, and the subcaudals are keeled. These are arboreal, mainly diurnal, oviparous snakes, which prey on lizards and frogs.

Striped Bronzeback *Dendrelaphis caudolineatus* to 152cm

Merel J. Cox

The head of this active snake is bronze, its supralabials greenish-yellow. Along each side of the grey-green body is a white stripe with a broad black border below and a narrow black edge above. The venter is greenish-yellow. A black line extends through the middle of the subcaudals to the tip of the tail. This hill snake is found up to 1,100m, usually on trees and bushes in well-watered forests and cultivated areas but occasionally foraging on the ground. Hatchlings, 35cm long, emerge from clutches of 5–8 eggs. It occurs in much of tropical Asia including southern Thailand, Malaysia and Singapore.

Wall's Bronzeback *Dendrelaphis cyanochloris* to 130cm

Romulus Whitaker

The slender body of of this attractive snake is olive with a characteristic net-like pattern formed by the black edges of the smooth body scales. A broad, black stripe extends from the head, through the neck, and on to the body, where it breaks up and disappears. The labials and chin are yellowish, as are the ventral surface and the throat. This snake is usually seen on bushes and trees, but it also forages on the ground. It ranges from sea level to 3,000m. It occurs in the northeast and south of Thailand and in Myanmar, Bangladesh, northeastern India and the Andaman and Nicobar Islands.

Elegant Bronzeback *Dendrelaphis formosus* to 156cm

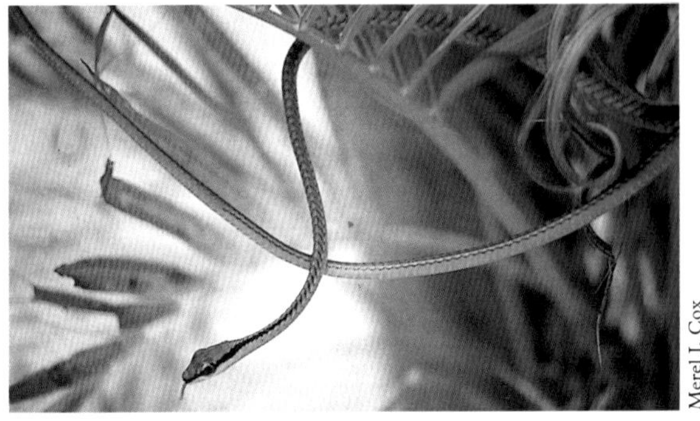

Merel J. Cox

The body of this elegant snake is bronze to light brown, occasionally with small blue or green spots on the sides and black lines on the posterior flanks. The head is reddish-brown, the neck is a deeper shade of red. A black stripe runs from the snout, through the eyes and along the neck. The throat and anterior ventral shields are light green; the posterior ventrals are dull green or brownish. This handsome snake inhabits rainforests up to 1,100m. Clutches of 6–8 eggs are incubated for 13–17 weeks before 30cm long hatchlings appear. It ranges from Phuket through Malaysia and Singapore east to Borneo and Java.

Common, or **Painted, Bronzeback**
Dendrelaphis pictus to 143cm

Wolfgang Wüster

This is the most common and widespread bronzeback in the region. It is characterized by the bronze upper body and head, the black face mask, which extends to the neck, and the yellow or cream stripe on the first two scale rows of the body, which is bordered above and below by a black line. The sides of the head and the chin are white. Blue spots show when the body expands when inhaling and when threatening. The venter is yellow to pale green. This graceful snake inhabits a variety of habitats in plains and hills up to at least 1,300m. Lizards, tree frogs and paddy frogs are its main prey. Females produce 2–10 eggs per clutch; hatchlings are about 25cm long. It ranges over much of tropical Asia.

Cohn's Bronzeback *Dendrelaphis striatus* to 100cm

Ulrich Manthey

The dorsal surface of this handsome bronzeback is bronze with a characteristic series of narrow, black, vertical bars on each side of the anterior portion of the body. Black and white lateral stripes are not found on this snake. A rather wide, black line extends from the snout, back through the eye, on to the neck. The labials and throat are yellow and the ventral surface grey or very light brown. This is another agile, arboreal member of the genus that can occasionally be found foraging on the ground. Cohn's Bronzeback is found in southern Thailand, Peninsular Malaysia and Sumatra, but it is not common.

Mountain Bronzeback *Dendrelaphis subocularis* to 113cm

Merel J. Cox

This bronzeback has distinctive black edges to the bronze body scales, which create the impression of thin, discontinuous lines along the body. The head and neck are olive green and the ventral surface is white. A cream-coloured line runs the length of the body through the scales bordering the ventrals. There is no black line on the edge of the ventrals. The keeled and notched ventrals and subcaudals enable this and other bronzebacks to climb vertical tree trunks with astonishing ease. The Mountain Bronzeback is found on forested plains and hills up to 460m throughout Thailand as far south as Chumphon, and in Myanmar, Yunnan and Indo-China.

REAR-FANGED SNAKES (Genus *Boiga*)

These are nocturnal, mainly arboreal, oviparous snakes. The slender, slightly compressed body has smooth scales whose vertebral series is usually enlarged. The snout is rounded, and the large distinct head has large shields and large eyes with distinct vertical pupils. The last two or three fangs at the end of the upper jaw are enlarged and grooved. These snakes produce **mild venom** which flows along the grooves to wounds inflicted by the rear fangs as the snake chews its prey. They feed on a variety of animals, including small mammals, birds, eggs and other reptiles including snakes. There have not been any fatalities attributed to the rear-fanged snakes in our area and none is considered dangerous.

White-spotted Cat Snake *Boiga drapiezii* to 210cm

Wolfgang Wüster

Wolfgang Wüster

(Above) *Green colour phase;* (below) *brown colour phase*

This beautiful snake occurs in two colour phases. One is predominantly green with irregular bands of green, tan, and pink on the body, while the head is dark green with some pink and white on the supralabials. The other colour phase is dominated by brown: the body has alternating dark- and light-brown bands, and the head is dark brown with white supralabials. Both phases have white infralabials, chin, and throat. This snake is at home in humid, forested areas, up to 1,100m. Clutches of up to 10 eggs are sometimes laid in arboreal termite nests. Hatchlings are about 30cm long. This species occurs in southern Thailand, Peninsular Malaysia, Singapore, Borneo, Indonesia east to Java and the southern Philippines.

Green Cat Snake *Boiga cyanea* to 187cm

Wolfgang Wüster

The head and long body of the Green Cat Snake are olive-green with a greyish or bluish hue above; the belly is yellowish anteriorly and whitish posteriorly. The chin and throat are white with a bluish tint. The ventrals have an indistinct lateral keel. This attractive snake inhabits forests up to 2,100m. It is occasionally found on the ground at night. Females lay 4–13 eggs per clutch; the light brown, reddish or pink hatchlings may have dark brown cross-bars and are about 35cm long. It resides in Thailand south to Phuket, as well as Assam, Myanmar, southern China and Indo-China.

Banded Green Cat Snake *Boiga saengsomi* to 162cm

Piboon Jintakune

This recently discovered snake has yellowish-green body scales with black skin visible between the scales. There are small, alternating yellow bands around the body. The tail is black with a central yellow dot. The head is olive, although here, too, black skin is visible between the scales. The supralabials are yellow, the chin and throat white, the ventral surface yellowish-white. This rare and attractive snake is known to inhabit well-watered forest at 150–170m above mean sea level. During the day it rests in trees and bushes. Its distribution is limited to southern Thailand.

Mangrove Snake *Boiga dendrophila melanota* to 250cm

The head is black and the yellow supralabials have black edges. The body and tail are glossy black with 21–41 narrow yellow bars which do not usually meet over the back. The throat and anterior ventrals are uniformly yellow, the remainder black with yellow. The Mangrove Snake is fond of humid forests and is often found on branches near or overhanging water at elevations up to 610m. From 4 to 15 large eggs are laid; young of 35–43cm resembling adults hatch after about 12 weeks. It occurs in southern Thailand, Peninsular Malaysia, Singapore and part of Sumatra.

Black-headed, or **Red, Cat Snake** *Boiga nigriceps* to 175cm

The body colour of this species ranges from grey- or reddish-brown to intense bright red. The head is usually dark brownish-red to olive. Occasionally, individuals have small black dots on the flanks. The labials are creamy white; the ventral surface is pink or dark yellow. This species prefers humid, well-watered, forested foothills up to 1,100m. It preys on lizards, birds, mice and probably on frogs and other snakes. A clutch of 3 eggs is known; hatchlings are about 40cm long and resemble adults. It occurs in southern Thailand, Malaysia and Indonesia east to Java.

Dog-toothed Cat Snake *Boiga cynodon* to 277cm

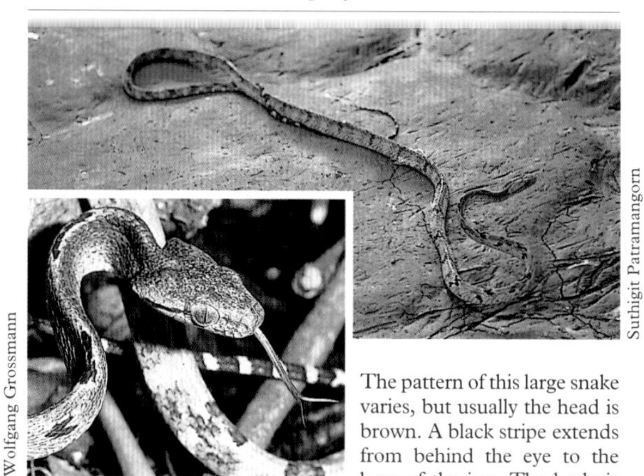

Suthigit Patramangorn

Wolfgang Grossmann

The pattern of this large snake varies, but usually the head is brown. A black stripe extends from behind the eye to the base of the jaw. The body is light brown with a variable pattern of dark-brown or black crossbars that become progressively more closely spaced posteriorly until the colour becomes almost solid at the tail. The ventrals are grey-brown and the subcaudals are black. Melanistic specimens are relatively common. Clutches of 6–12 eggs produce hatchlings similar to adults. This snake inhabits lowlands of Thailand south of 8°N, Malaysia, Singapore, Indonesia east to Flores and the Philippines.

Marble, Many-spotted, or **Spotted, Cat Snake**
Boiga multomaculata to 187cm

Wolfgang Wüster

The colour and pattern of this attractive snake often results in confusion with the venomous, stout, terrestrial Russell's Viper. The upper head and body are grey-brown. Two paired rows of elongated, black-edged, brown markings cover the body; those on the sides are slightly smaller than those on the back. The venter is grey-brown and peppered with small brown spots. This distinctive cat snake inhabits well-watered forests from sea level to 1,210m. Females produce 4–8 eggs per clutch, hatchlings measure 20cm. It occurs widely in Southeast Asia including Peninsular Malaysia, Singapore and Thailand except the south.

Grey Cat Snake *Boiga ocellata* to 170cm

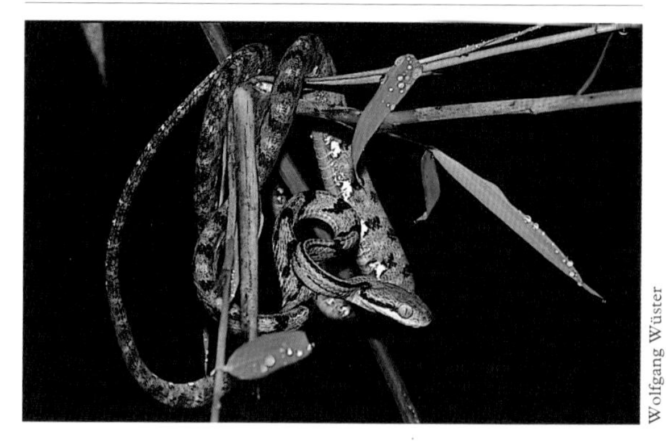

Wolfgang Wüster

The Grey Cat Snake resembles the Dog-toothed Cat Snake but it occupies a different geographical range. Its body is greyish-brown with black crossbars that are most distinct anteriorly. The head is dark brown with a dark streak from behind the eye to the first body crossbar that is broken just beyond the last supralabial. The chin and throat are white, the ventrals white to light brown. This species is found on plains and forested hills up to 1,780m. Its diet is known to include birds and eggs. It occurs in Thailand north of the Kra Isthmus, in Indo-China, Myanmar and nearby areas.

Jasper Cat Snake *Boiga jaspidea* to 150cm

Piboon Jintakune

The reddish-brown body has irregular black and thin pinkish-white lines on the vertebral ridge. There are black-based white or yellow dots on the sides of the body. The head is brown with a pattern of white-edged black spots. The labials are white but crossed by black spots. The throat and the anterior third of the ventral surface are yellow; the remainder is light brown. This handsome snake prefers humid, well-watered areas at elevations up to 1,100m. Clutches of 6 eggs, laid in arboreal termite nests, and 40cm hatchlings resembling adults are known. It occurs in southern Thailand, Malaysia, Singapore and Indonesia east to Kalimantan and Java.

ASIATIC SLUG SNAKES (Subfamily Pareatinae)

Most members of this subfamily are primarily arboreal and prey on snails and slugs. The chin shields extend irregularly across the middle of the throat and there is no median groove. The head is distinct and the eyes have vertical pupils. These snakes are oviparous. Two genera with eight species inhabit our area.

Blunt-headed Slug Snake *Aplopeltura boa* to 84cm

Piboon Jintakune

The vertebral scales on the slender body are quite enlarged and the body scales smooth. The body is yellowish, greyish or pale brown with darker brown blotches. The short, blunt and proportionally large head has a large brown or reddish blotch on top and a dark mark beneath the eye. The lips are white. This arboreal snake occurs up to 1,300m and eats slugs, snails and lizards. Clutches contain 4–8 eggs; hatchlings are about 20cm long and resemble adults. It inhabits southern Thailand, Peninsular Malaysia and areas further east.

Keeled Slug Snake *Pareas carinatus* to 60cm

Anita Malhotra

A fairly common snake with short snout and blunt head. The body is strongly compressed, the scales slightly keeled, and the vertebral scales enlarged. The body is brown with dark markings. A black streak runs back from each eye to a distinctive X-shaped mark on the nape. This nocturnal, semi-arboreal snake inhabits deciduous forests up to 1,780m. Clutches of 3–5 eggs are laid; the hatchlings are 16cm long and resemble adults. It can be found on the ground at night foraging for prey. It occurs widely, including northern Peninsular Malaysia and all areas of Thailand except the Central Plain.

White-spotted, or **Northern Mountain, Slug Snake**
Pareas margaritophorus to 47cm

Wolfgang Wüster

This mostly grey species shows distinctive transverse series of white and black spots together on single scales. A white or yellow nuchal collar may be present. The ventrals are whitish, usually spotted with grey or black. The body is somewhat compressed with smooth scales and the vertebrals are not enlarged. This terrestrial and nocturnal snake inhabits evergreen forests in hilly country up to 1,640m. It preys on snails and slugs. Hatchlings are 7–10cm long. It occurs from southern China to northern Peninsular Malaysia.

Southern Mountain, or **Vertebral, Slug Snake**
Pareas vertebralis to 76cm

Gernot Vogel

This slug snake's body is compressed, the vertebral scales are slightly enlarged, and the centre of the back forms a sharp ridge. The head shields and eye are large. The ventrals are rounded. Adults are usually uniform brown, slightly paler below, while some have a pale vertebral stripe and distinct dark spots on the sides. Some are yellowish below. Young specimens have dark transverse bands extending to the venter, and a pale vertebral stripe. Active at night and semi-arboreal, this snake has been found at 1,640m. Clutches of 2–6 eggs are known. It occurs in the mountain areas of Peninsular Malaysia and Sabah.

GECKOS (Family Gekkonidae)

The geckos form a distinctive family of relatively small lizards; the Tockay gecko of the region is one of the largest species. Several gecko groups have developed highly specialized digital pads, or scansors, under their fingers and toes. These consist of expanded, flattened surfaces bearing countless fine projections (called setae), each in turn branching into hundreds of bristles terminating in fine endplates. This provides grip on the finest of minute irregularities, permitting the animal to move confidently even on the underside of smooth surfaces. Sharp claws provide grip on rough surfaces. The genera of geckos are identified by the development of the toes. Geckos inhabit a variety of habitats, but all eat insects and other small animal prey, and all are oviparous, typically laying two eggs at a time. Most geckos are able to make clicking sounds, while a few have distinctive loud calls that confirm the presence of a cryptic animal at once. The head and body scales of geckos are typically small and granular with larger, often tubercular scales scattered among them. A gecko can easily and promptly shed its tail in case of attack; this is done by the lizard contracting its muscles to break a vertebra along a breakage plane, rather than by physical force of a predator pulling. Often the slightest touch to a stressed gecko's tail is enough to cause it to drop its tail. The skin of the body also tears very easily, permitting escape even when held at the body. Therefore, employ maximum caution and restraint when attempting to handle geckos.

Flat-tailed Gecko *Cosymbotus platyurus*

SVL to 6cm, total to 12.5cm

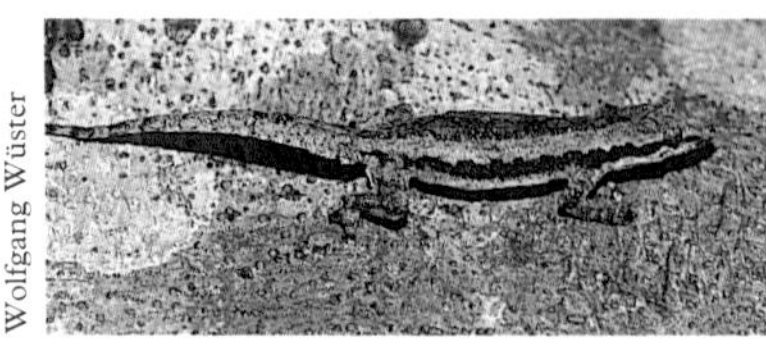

Wolfgang Wüster

This abundant gecko is recognized by its flattened tail, the webbing at the base of the fingers and toes, and the fringe of skin along the body. The coloration varies greatly, from uniform pale grey, through mottled brownish-grey, to a series of distinct, dark, diamond marks and a dark flank band on a grey base. It is often active during daylight, as well as at night. It occurs in a wide variety of habitats, from dry forests to human habitations. It feeds on a variety of insects, as well as spiders. Its call is a soft, rapid '*djieb-djieb-djieb*', and a buzz. This gecko is common throughout Thailand, Malaysia and Singapore, and most of tropical Asia.

Kuhl's Gliding Gecko *Ptychozoon kuhlii*
SVL to 9.5cm, total to 19cm

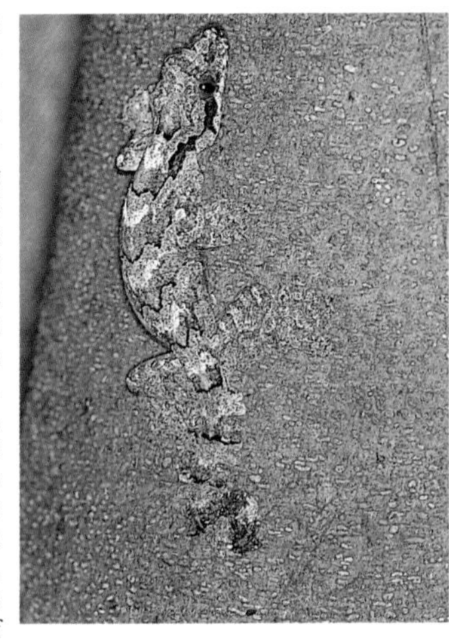

The gliding geckos of the genus *Ptychozoon* are characterized by their moderately large size, a wide skin flap along the flank, additional skin flaps along the limbs and neck, and extensively webbed hands and feet. The original tail has a fringe of rounded separate lappets, but regenerated tails show a single continuous fringe. The inner digit is clawless, the others bear a large claw; the distal phalanges are subsumed in the expanded portion, which bears undivided scansors. Diagnostic features of this species are the presence of large granules scattered over the back, and the lappets of the tail oriented at right angles to the tail. It inhabits little-disturbed, closed, evergreen forests, usually near streams. It occurs from southern Thailand through Malaysia, the Nicobars, Sumatra to Borneo, and Java.

Smooth-backed Gliding Gecko *Ptychozoon lionotum*
SVL to 10cm, total to 19cm

This species is very similar to Kuhl's Gliding Gecko, from which it differs by having the tail lappets directed somewhat backwards, the absence of enlarged tubercles on the dorsum, and the first finger separated from the skin flap along the forearm. It also appears more slender and less intensively patterned. It shares its habitat with the preceding species. Normally active at night, it can occasionally be seen resting on a tree trunk by day. When pursued, it jumps off and uses the skin fringes to glide to another tree, or at least break its fall. It occurs from Myanmar to Vietnam and Borneo.

Tockay *Gekko gecko* SVL to 18cm, total to 35cm

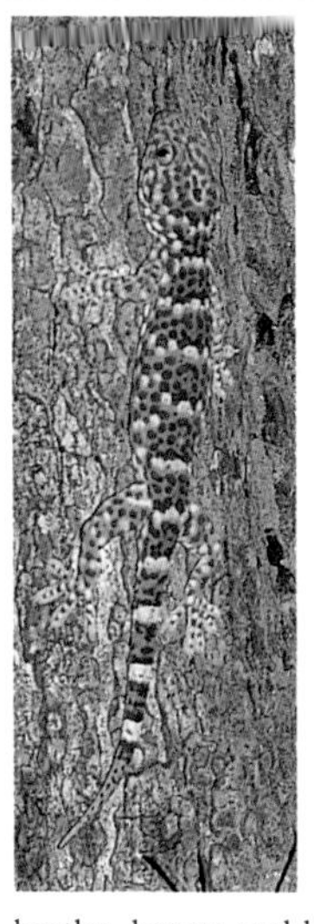

Henrik Bringsøe

One of the most distinctive lizards of Southeast Asia, the orange- or red-spotted Tockay is more often heard than seen. During part of the year, males give an unmistakable, loud call, '*túc-kèh*', repeated several times; females do not call. Normally territorial, these animals sometimes live in small family groups consisting of a male, female and immature offspring. At night they hunt on houses or trees, foraging or ambushing; during the day they rest in a crevice. Food consists mainly of large insects, such as large beetles, locusts and large winged termites, but other types of prey are taken as well. Clutches of 2, rarely 3, eggs are plastered to solid surfaces. The Tockay occurs throughout eastern tropical Asia.

Forest Gecko *Gekko smithi* SVL to 16cm, total to 30cm

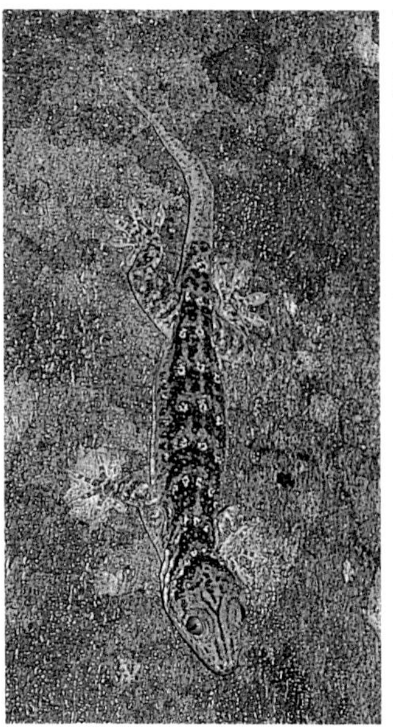

This large gecko is similar to the Tockay, but it has green eyes, a less bulky head, and lacks orange spots. The call differs as well, being a loud '*túk, túk, túk*'. Like all members of the genus *Gekko*, the distal part of each digit is subsumed into the dilated portion which bears undivided scansors. The outer four digits bear strong claws; the inner digit is well developed but without a claw. This strictly nocturnal species prefers little-disturbed forested areas, living on and in trees and rarely entering human habitations. It occurs in rainforest from extreme southern Thailand through Malaysia and Singapore into Indonesia, as well as the Andaman Islands.

Spotted House Gecko *Gekko monarchus*
SVL to 10cm, total to 22cm

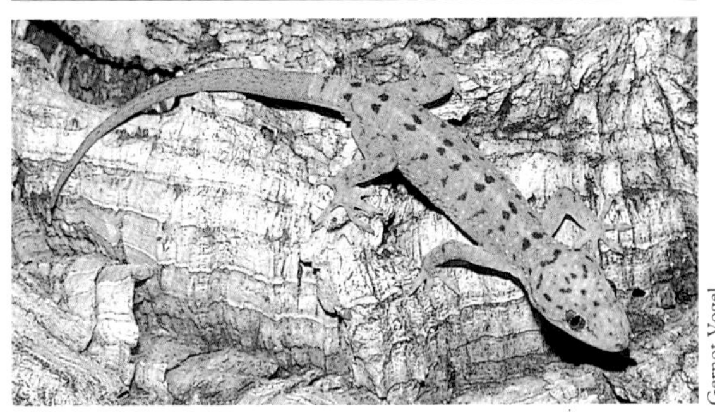

Gernot Vogel

Pale grey or fawn colour, with pairs of dark blotches over the spine, is typical for this moderate-sized gecko. The dorsal tubercles are distinctly enlarged and strongly convex to conical; the rostral contacts the nostril. Males have a preanofemoral pore series with 16–20 pores on each side. This is mainly a species of tall evergreen, lowland rainforest, although it is also at home in human habitations close to forest. It is active at night, yet calls most frequently at twilight. Eggs are laid in pairs, hidden in decaying logs and forest litter. It occurs from the extreme south of Thailand, through Peninsular Malaysia and Singapore to New Guinea and the Philippines.

Sandstone Gecko *Gekko petricolus* SVL to 10cm, total to 21cm

This moderate-sized gecko represents a group of slender *Gekko* species whose rostral scale contacts the nostril, and in whom there are no strongly spiny tubercles on the back or tail, and the coloration is a variation on the theme of greenish-yellow with vague darker bands and pale spots. This group has its distribution centred on the Annamitic mountain chain in Laos, Vietnam and Cambodia, and only the Sandstone Gecko is found in northeastern Thailand, adjacent Laos and presumably Cambodia. It inhabits cracks in weathered sandstone, but occasionally uses man-made equivalents such as unoccupied brick buildings. It is usually seen upside-down in pairs or groups. The small eggs are plastered in rock crevices.

Spiny-tailed House Gecko *Hemidactylus frenatus*
SVL to 6cm, total to 13cm

Probably the region's most common house gecko, this species is characterized by the whorls of small spines on the original tail, small rounded tubercles mixed in with the granules on the back, and its inner toe, bearing a large claw, being less than half the length of the second toe. The colour ranges through various shades of brown, either uniform or with darker markings. It is nocturnal, but sometimes seen in the late afternoon, while its harsh chirping call can be heard at any time. This gecko feeds on small insects, often on ceilings and walls near electric lights. Clutches of 2 spherical eggs are hidden in a crevice; hatchlings are miniature replicas of adults. This species occurs in much of tropical Asia.

Garnot's Gecko *Hemidactylus garnotii*
SVL to 6.5cm, total to 15cm

This gecko is relatively flattened, with a long, pointed snout and a strongly depressed tail which bears a distinct series of lateral serrations. It is brownish-grey above, often with fine darker markings and pale spots, and yellow ventrally. It lives on tree trunks, rock outcrops and on buildings. This is a parthenogenic species, females producing 2 fertile eggs per clutch without the involvement of a male; all hatchlings are female. Consequently, this species easily establishes itself and has been reported from a wide range of locations, from India and China through Southeast Asia and widely among the islands of the Pacific. On the mainland, it is uncommon and localized.

Four-clawed Gecko *Gehyra mutilata*
SVL to 6cm, total to 12cm

This delicate gecko can be recognized by the absence of a free terminal phalange on the inner finger and toe; the inner digit may have a minute claw, or none. The distal parts of the clawed outer four digits arise distinctly from the widely expanded pads under the toes. The head is proportionally large and rounded, the blotched pale grey skin delicately granular, and the tail flattened, usually widened at its base and with a finely denticulate edge. This species is occasionally seen inside old houses, although it naturally inhabits hollow trees. Besides the usual insects and other small invertebrates, the Four-clawed Gecko apparently also feeds on fruit juice and nectar. It ranges widely from Myanmar to Oceania.

Miniature Gecko *Hemiphyllodactylus typus*
SVL to 5cm, total to 10cm

Ulrich Manthey

The small size and distinctive colour pattern identify this gecko at a glance. A dark-brown stripe runs from each nostril, along the side of the head and neck to the shoulder, and a characteristic dark-edged creamy mark on the tail base extends forward; the tail may be variegated brown or uniform cream. The body is slender, the limbs are short, and the inner digit is vestigial, as is typical of the genus. This gecko inhabits various forest types, especially mangroves. It is nocturnal, foraging in trees and spending the daytime hidden in crevices. It ranges widely, from Sri Lanka to Oceania, but is very localized in its occurrence.

Banded Slender-toed Gecko *Cyrtodactylus pulchellus*
SVL to 11.5cm, total to 26cm

Wolfgang Wüster

This stunning tan gecko with dark brown bands shows both the slender toes without expanded scansors and the vertical pupils that are characteristic of its genus. Males have two series of four pre-anal pores in a deep longitudinal groove, connected at right angles to a series of 15–20 femoral pores. It inhabits moist evergreen rainforest, occurring up to 2,000m altitude. Animals are active at dusk and at night on tree trunks, the forest floor and cave walls, where they feed on crickets and other insects. Clutches of 2 eggs are buried in the soil; hatchlings emerge after five to seven months and are 6–7cm long. It occurs in Peninsular Thailand and Malaysia and possibly also in Singapore.

Cardamom Slender-toed Gecko *Cyrtodactylus intermedius*
SVL to 8.5cm, total to 19cm

Jarujin Nabhitabhata

This beautiful gecko is very similar to the Banded Slender-toed Gecko in appearance, but differs fundamentally in the arrangement of the male pores: there are eight or ten pores in a wide-angled series before the vent, followed by a group of enlarged preanal scales, and a series of six to ten enlarged femoral scales under the upper leg. There is a skin fold between the flank and the venter. This species lives in seasonal evergreen forest at moderate altitudes. Nocturnal in its activities, it spends the daytime hidden under the loose bark of rotting logs and in other crevices. It is restricted to the mountain ranges of eastern Thailand and southern Cambodia.

Large-spotted Slender-toed Gecko *Cyrtodactylus peguensis*
SVL to 8cm, total to 18cm

Wolfgang Wüster

Besides the gorgeous colour pattern of yellow or pinkish brown networking lines isolating pairs of large round dark brown or black spots on the head and back, and the bold dark band around the back of the head, this gecko is recognized by the widened scales under the tail and the seven to nine preanal pores arranged in a wide angle. It inhabits hill areas at moderate altitude, where it is occasionally found in dense vegetation and accumulated leaf litter among tree buttresses in evergreen forest. It occurs in western and peninsular Thailand south to Phatthalung, and in Pegu and Tenasserim in Myanmar.

Barred Slender-toed Gecko *Cyrtodactylus variegatus*
SVL to 7cm, total to 17cm

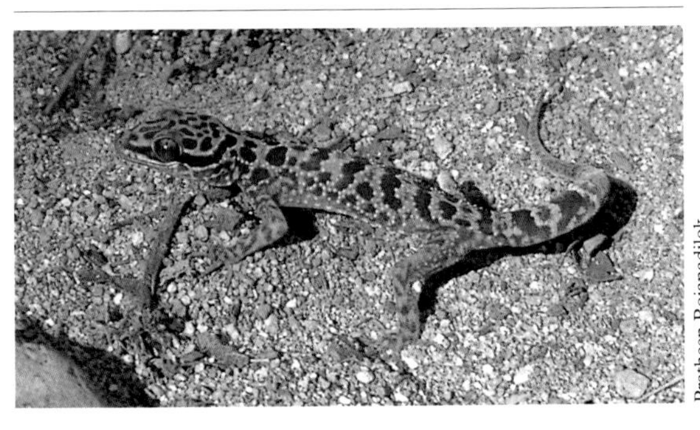

Pratheep Rojanadilok

The dorsal colour pattern of irregular dark and light bars, the large rounded ventral scales (of which there are only about 22 across the venter) and the continuous series of about 32 preanal and femoral pores are diagnostic. Enlarged tubercles occur scattered over the back. This species inhabits large caves on mountain slopes, hiding inside during the day and emerging at night to forage around the cave entrance. The animals live in family groups. Until recently, this rare gecko was known only from two specimens collected in southeastern Myanmar. It has since been found in northern and western Thailand.

Peters' Slender-toed Gecko *Cyrtodactylus consobrinus*
SVL to 12cm, total to 28cm

Ulrich Manthey

Juveniles of this beautiful gecko are pure black with irregular white or cream lines and reticulation; with growth, the dark areas fade at their centres and adults appear to have black-edged cream lines on a finely speckled brown body. This is a rainforest species, at home in lowlands and at moderate elevations. It emerges late in the evening from its hiding place to sit on tree trunks and wait for prey to pass by; its coloration closely matches tree bark. Clutches of two eggs are laid. This beautiful species occurs from extreme southern Thailand to Sumatra, Borneo and Singkep.

Web-footed Slender-toed Gecko
Cyrtodactylus brevipalmatus SVL to 7cm, total to 16cm

Ulrich Manthey

This rare gecko is one of very few *Cyrtodactylus* species to have webbed feet. It is further characterized by a slightly spiky tail and numerous small tubercles on its back. Its coloration is uniform brown above, or may show some darker brown angular markings; the tail is banded and the undersurfaces are creamy white. This rare gecko inhabits forests up to 900m, usually near streams. Animals have been found under dead tree bark, in tree cavities and among tangled root masses. Its range is limited to southern Thailand and perhaps northern Peninsular Malaysia.

Marbled Slender-toed Gecko *Cyrtodactylus quadrivirgatus*
SVL to 7cm, total to 14cm

Ulrich Manthey

This pretty gecko is typified by the absence of some characteristics: it does not possess spiny tubercles either on the ventrolateral folds or on the tail; it has no enlarged subcaudals and no pubic groove; males lack femoral pores, and at most four preanal pores may be present. The dorsal coloration is fawn to dark brown with darker markings, usually arranged in longitudinal series or lines. The scales around the eye and tubercles on the sides of the head and flanks may be yellowish. A moderately common inhabitant of open or disturbed forest, this gecko perches on tree trunks, saplings and high earth-banks along streams and trails. It occurs in far southern Thailand, Peninsular Malaysia and Singapore.

Siamese Leaf-toed Gecko *Phyllodactylus siamensis*
SVL to 5cm, total to 11cm

Jarujin Nabhitabhata

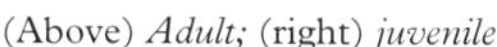
(Above) *Adult;* (right) *juvenile*

A delightful small gecko with long, slender, clawed digits which bear a single widened scansor under the tip. There are many longitudinal series of large tubercles on the back and flanks, but not above the spine. Juveniles are almost black with paired series of white spots on the back; with age, the dark coloration bleaches and adults are tan or pinkish with some dorsal dark markings. It inhabits a variety of forest types, occasionally in developed areas, where it hides under rotting wood by day, and forages on the ground or low on tree trunks at night, presumably for termites. Females lay clutches of 2 eggs during the rainy season. It occurs in much of Thailand and southern Myanmar, Vietnam and Laos, but it is not known in Malaysia.

Wandering Round-eyed Gecko *Cnemaspis kandianus*
SVL to 4cm, total to 8.5cm

The geckos of the genus *Cnemaspis* are characterized by their round pupils and slender, clawed digits. This species shows distinct white-tipped conical tubercles on the flank, and smooth ventral and proximal subcaudal scales, the distal ones being keeled; the proximal subdigital scales are much larger than the distal ones. Males have both preanal and femoral pores. This gecko inhabits forest and disturbed human habitats. It is terrestrial or associated with fallen logs; it may on occasion be observed during the day. It occurs strongly localized in southern Thailand, the Andaman and Mentawei Islands, and Sri Lanka and southern India; it is most likely that it has been introduced to some of these areas among ships' cargo.

Dark Round-eyed Gecko *Cnemaspis nigridius*
SVL to 8cm, total to 14cm

Ulrich Manthey

This is one of the largest round-eyed geckos, making it somewhat easier to identify. The ventrals are keeled, and the median subcaudals are smooth, rounded and flat. The fourth finger is distinctly longer than the fifth. This gecko species occurs on Pulau Tioman off the Pahang coast of Malaysia, on Bunguran in the Natuna group of islands, and in Sarawak on Borneo. Its close relative, KENDALL'S ROUND-EYED GECKO (*C. kendalli*) matures at a smaller size, reaching only 58mm SVL. It is blotchy grey-brown just like the Dark Round-eyed Gecko. It differs chiefly in having a more spiky tail with the median subcaudals keeled, pointed and raised. It occurs on the mainland of Peninsular Malaysia and in Singapore.

Siamese Round-eyed Gecko *Cnemaspis siamensis*
SVL to 4cm, total to 9cm

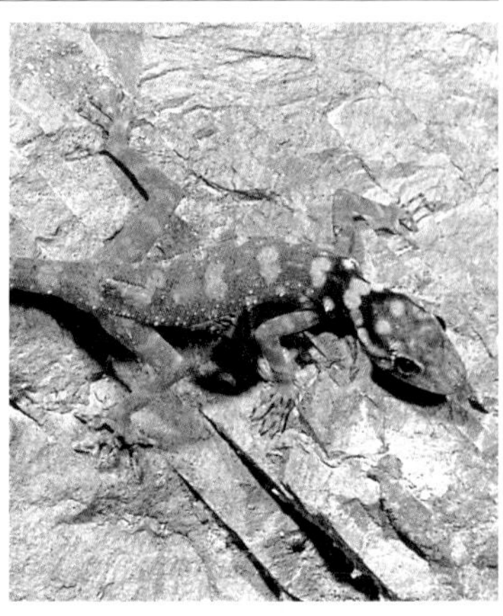
Ulrich Manthey

This delicate little gecko is most easily recognized by the distinctive colour pattern of black and white bands and spots on the head and neck. The chin and chest of breeding adults are bright yellow. The fifth, outer finger is about equal in size to the fourth. The back is covered with small granules that are intermixed with much larger, keeled tubercles. The ventral scales are keeled, while the median subcaudals form a series of enlarged, keeled, weakly pointed scales. Males usually have between two and eight preanal pores. This delightful species is at home on rocks and tree trunks, especially those with large buttresses. It is active both by day and at night; it is swift to hide in cracks. It occurs in southern Thailand, ranging from the Isthmus of Kra to the Thai-Malay border.

Cat-eyed Gecko *Aeluroscalabotes felinus*
SVL to 11cm, total to 18cm

Merel J. Cox

This remarkable gecko is the only species in the region to possess eyelids and to be capable of closing its eyes. All five digits bear a large claw that can be retracted between three large scales. The body is slender, the head disproportionally large, and the slender limbs are long while the rather fat tail is short. The back may be unpatterned or may show irregular longitudinal light bands, which sometimes fragment to form series of white dots. This gecko inhabits damp, undisturbed and secondary rainforest, presumably close to streams, foraging at night in the undergrowth. It includes spiders and crickets in its diet. This rare species inhabits extreme southern Thailand, Malaysia and Borneo.

AGAMA LIZARDS (Family Agamidae)

The agamid lizards occur in tropical and temperate Asia, Australia and Africa (except Madagascar), where they are often the dominant lizard group in terms of diversity and abundance. Agamids are characterized by a generally spiky and spindly appearance. In detail, they have small irregular scales on the head and often bear spiny crests on the neck, spine and tail; the body scales are often large, pointed, keeled and overlapping, and there is an expandable sac or fan under the throat which is usually best developed in mature males. The long tail does not break easily but can be regenerated in case this happens. The teeth are typically diversified into forms resembling incisors, canines and molars, and larger agamids can deliver a painful bite. Typically, agamids are terrestrial or arboreal; they have radiated into a great diversity of arboreal forms in tropical Asia, culminating in the incredible gliding lizards of the genus *Draco*. Nearly all species are active by day and feed on insects and other small animal prey; nearly all species are oviparous. Most species can quickly and dramatically change colours in response to emotional and environmental challenges.

Horned Tree Lizard *Acanthosaura armata*
SVL to 12cm, total to 29cm

Jarujin Nabhitabhata

(Above) *Male;* (left) *female*

The *Acanthosaura* species have moderately compressed bodies and vertebral crests formed by a single row of scales. In this species the distinctive features are the long spines behind the orbit and on the side of the neck (which in adults are as tall as the diameter of the eye), the high nuchal and dorsal spiny crests, and the naked tympanum. The Horned Tree Lizard is usually seen at rest low on slender trees in rainforest. It is reputed to feed mainly on earthworms. Females lay between 9 and 15 eggs per clutch. This spectacular lizard inhabits Thailand south from Nakhon Si Thammarat through Malaysia and perhaps Singapore to Sumatra.

Cross-bearing Tree Lizard *Acanthosaura crucigera*
SVL to 10cm, total to 25cm

The distinction between this species and the Scale-bellied Tree Lizard is not very clear: the Cross-bearing Lizard possesses a naked tympanum and a black diamond shoulder mark connecting to diagonal marks below, but whether these differences permit reliable differentiation is debatable. Both forms have head and neck spines and dorsal crests of similar arrangement and size, while coloration is variable in both. This lizard occurs in monsoon evergreen hill forest, where it lives on the forest floor among dense undergrowth. Earthworms may form an important part of the diet. Females lay clutches of about 10 eggs. This form is understood to inhabit eastern, western and peninsular Thailand and adjacent Tenasserim.

Scale-bellied Tree Lizard *Acanthosaura lepidogaster*
SVL to 9cm, total to 27cm

This form differs chiefly from the Cross-bearing Tree Lizard by having the outer part of tympanum covered with small scales. Usually it has a Y-shaped series of scales on the snout and frontal area. There is a small spine behind the eye and another spine, or a small cluster, on the neck; the crest of broad-based compressed scales on the neck is usually narrowly separated from the low crest on the back. Its food consists mainly of hymenopteran insect larvae, while winged termites are also eaten. A clutch may contain up to 11 eggs. This attractive lizard occurs in northern and western Thailand and nearby areas of Myanmar, China and Indo-China.

Bell's Anglehead Lizard *Gonocephalus bellii*
SVL to 14cm, total to 47cm

Ulrich Manthey

Male

The *Gonocephalus* lizards are distinguished by their strongly compressed bodies and tails, body scales irregular in size and arrangement, a strong skin fold across the throat and the male's possession of a gular pouch and a tall vertebral crest that is usually composed of several rows of enlarged scales. Bell's Anglehead Lizard has strongly keeled dorsal, gular and ventral scales, the ridge over the eye is not strongly elevated, enlarged scales occur scattered over its flanks and it has continuous nuchal and dorsal crests of spiky scales which become very high in males. Females lay 3–5 eggs. It inhabits undisturbed rainforest at low and moderate altitudes in southern Thailand, Malaysia and Borneo.

Great Anglehead Lizard *Gonocephalus grandis*
SVL to 16cm, total to 55cm

Ulrich Manthey

Male in stress colour

Males of this impressive lizard have separate, very high, ribbon-like crests on the neck and back composed of long, basally united spines. The flanks bear no enlarged scales, the ventral scales are smooth, and the eyebrow ridge is not particularly enlarged. Like most *Gonocephalus* species, the female is somewhat smaller than the male. When at rest the animals are shades of brown with dark markings on the back, pale spots on the flanks and a pale throat; under stress males change to olive-green, females and juveniles to reddish-brown. Up to 6 eggs are laid in a clutch. This species prefers undisturbed streamside forest; it occurs in the far south of Thailand, Malaysia, Sumatra and in Borneo.

Chameleon Anglehead Lizard *Gonocephalus chamaeleontinus*
SVL to 17cm, total to 45cm

Ulrich Manthey

The strongly elevated eyebrow ridge and the tall spiky neck crest, which is much higher than the dorsal crest, typify this bizarre lizard. The ventral scales are smooth. Normally greenish, it can dramatically change colour to green, black, brown or tan. Males and females are generally similar in coloration and scale character, but females are somewhat smaller and may develop a tuberous growth on the snout tip. This territorial species is at home in primary rainforest, where it prefers to perch on moderate-sized tree trunks near streams. Females lay 3–7 eggs. This species occurs on Pulau Tioman, off Peninsular Malaysia, as well as on Sumatra, Java and nearby islands.

Doria's Anglehead Lizard *Gonocephalus doriae (G. abbotti)*
SVL to 16cm, total to 40cm

Ulrich Manthey

This beautiful lizard has strongly elevated ridges above its eyes. The crests on the neck and back are continuous and of similar height; they are formed by scales that are almost as wide as they are high, and that have a curved upper edge. The flank scales are smooth and fairly regular. Females are bright green, with black lines radiating from the eye and enlarged yellow scales on the flanks; mature males are brick red with some black. Little is known of the habits of this species; animals have been observed on tree trunks and saplings in the rainforest at moderate altitudes. It inhabits southern Thailand, Malaysia and Borneo.

Garden Fence Lizard *Calotes versicolor*
SVL to 9.5cm, total to 38cm

(Top) *Male in breeding colours;* (right) *juvenile*

This lizard's identity can be confirmed by its possession of two spines above the tympanum, the absence of spines behind the eye, and the absence of a shoulder fold. The male is somewhat larger than the female, and has strongly swollen cheeks and tail base. This lizard can change colour rapidly and dramatically, appearing uniform tan, marbled brown, or clouded grey with reddish, depending on emotions. It is a common sight in parks, gardens, agricultural areas, waste land and open forest, where it lives among leafy undergrowth and grass, although mature males often display from fences and other conspicuous places. The diet includes various insects, as well as other small animal prey. The male develops a reddish head and black blotch on the throat during the mating season, and displays its size and coloration to ward off other males and impress females. Early in the rainy season, females scratch out a hole in the ground using their forelimbs, where they lay 4–12 eggs before closing it and obliterating all traces. The oblong eggs measure about 14 × 8mm; hatchlings emerge after five to seven weeks and measure about 7cm (including the tail); they mature in about one year. This species is widely distributed from Sri Lanka and India throughout most of Southeast Asia to southern China including Hainan; it is absent from southern Peninsular Malaysia and was introduced to Singapore relatively recently.

Forest Crested Lizard *Calotes emma emma*
SVL to 10cm, total to 35cm

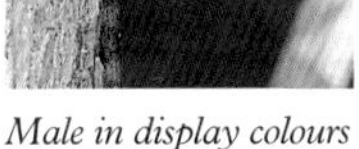

Male in display colours

Wolfgang Wüster

This beautiful lizard is characterized by the large spine above the eye, two spines above the tympanum, and by a skin fold before the shoulder which covers an area of small black scales. Like all *Calotes* species, the large dorsal and flank scales are regular in size, pointed, strongly keeled, and arranged in series where the keels point backwards and upwards. This subspecies has long head spines and is normally coloured soft green and grey with dark bars on the back. Males become much darker during the breeding season, showing a reddish throat pouch and black angular marks on the flanks. Females lay 4–12 eggs. This subspecies inhabits peninsular Thailand south to Perak in Malaysia.

Northern Forest Crested Lizard *Calotes emma alticristatus*
SVL to 12cm, total to 42cm

This northern subspecies of the Forest Crested Lizard is larger than the typical form, mature males have a more strongly developed vertebral crest, and the spines above and behind the eye are much smaller. When stressed, the animals show a deep orange head with black band through the eye, pale upper lip, and dark body with a bright-white or orange band over the flank. Like the typical form, this subspecies lives low on tree trunks, among undergrowth and forest litter, in closed, moist forest to about 900m altitude. Up to a dozen elliptical eggs, measuring 17× 11mm, are laid per clutch. This subspecies ranges from Assam and Yunnan through Southeast Asia to peninsular Thailand.

Male in display colours

Moustached, or **Blue Crested, Lizard** *Calotes mystaceus*
SVL to 14cm, total to 42cm

Both sexes of this spectacular lizard show the turquoise to blue body colour, white upper lip and reddish-brown blotches on the flank. Outside the breeding season, animals are variably brownish-grey with darker flank markings; the upper lip remains pale. Two small spines, or small groups of spines, occur above the tympanum. An area of small black scales is present before the shoulder. This species is more arboreal than other *Calotes* species in the region, hunting large insects on trunks of trees high above the ground. Females bury their eggs, about 7, after the first heavy rains of the year; juveniles emerge about two months later. It inhabits Myanmar, Thailand except the peninsula, and Indo-China.

Green Crested Lizard *Bronchocela cristatella*
SVL to 13cm, total to 58cm

Ulrich Manthey

The *Bronchocela* species have long heads, slender limbs and long tails. The uniform body scales point back and down, an oblique shoulder fold is absent, and the cheeks and tail base are never swollen in adult males. The Green Crested Lizard species is identified by its green colour with contrasting dark-brown ear, and by the tall neck crest of the male. Under stress it darkens to brown or dark grey. This arboreal lizard prefers undisturbed forest but may also be found in woodlands, parks and gardens. Females bury 2 large eggs in soil; hatchlings measure 35mm SVL. This attractive lizard inhabits southern Thailand, Malaysia, Singapore and Borneo.

Small-scaled Forest Lizard *Pseudocalotes microlepis*
SVL to 8.5cm, total to 27cm

The long, pointed snout, the short, weak limbs with the fourth toe equally long as the third, and the proportionally short tail are characteristic of the genus *Pseudocalotes*. This species is characterized by the keeled upper dorsal scales directed straight backwards, 65–72 small scales in a series around mid-body, and the sub-digital scales that are widened into blades. It is deliberate in its movements. Like its relatives, this species is capable of dramatic colour changes, changing from uniform pale brown when at rest to intense dark marbling when stressed. This delightful little lizard inhabits the undergrowth of montane forests above 1,100m altitude. It occurs on mountain slopes in northern Thailand and Myanmar.

Earless Lizard *Aphaniotus fuscus* SVL to 7cm, total to 22cm

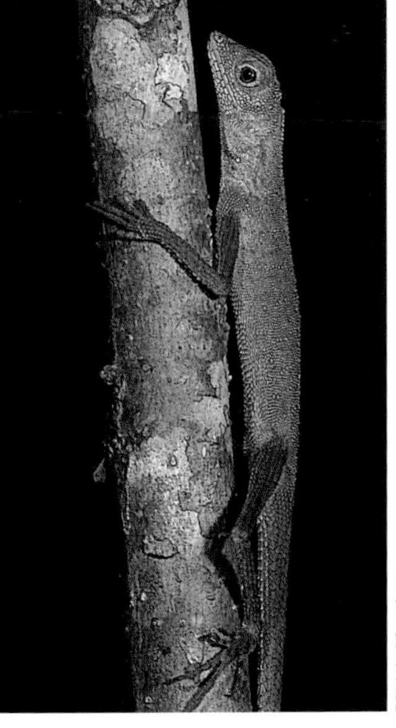

Ulrich Manthey

At first glance, this small lizard resembles a gliding lizard or a juvenile *Calotes*, but the absence of both a patagium and large keeled body scales suggest otherwise. The absence of an external ear, indicated only by an enlarged scale, the small body scales, and the barely developed vertebral crest clearly justify its placement in a separate genus. This spindly lizard inhabits undisturbed shaded rainforest, where it is occasionally seen perched on stems and leaves. Females lay 1 or 2 eggs. It occurs in the extreme southern part of Thailand, Peninsular Malaysia, Singapore, Borneo and the Natuna Islands.

GLIDING LIZARDS (Genus *Draco*)

The gliding lizards are unmistakable as a group: they are instantly recognized by their spindly appearance, the large and brightly coloured throat pouch of the males, and the wide patagium along each side of the body. The patagium is an expanse of skin supported by four to seven elongated ribs; by moving the ribs, the patagium can be folded along the body or expanded. Gliding lizards are almost exclusively arboreal, moving up tree trunks and using the outstretched patagium to sail to a lower position on the same or a nearby tree; they can glide significant distances, travelling up to 5m for every metre of height lost, and they can steer in mid-air. The animals are territorial, and display their throat fans, neck lappets and patagia to communicate with other gliding lizards. Females have only small dewlaps, or none at all. The eggs are buried in soil.

A total of 11 species of gliding lizard inhabit Thailand, Peninsular Malaysia and Singapore. Usually five to seven species co-exist in the peninsular rainforests. The various species are difficult to identify, and thus it is usually necessary to catch the specimen in order to examine such characters as the number of ribs in the patagium, the arrangement of scales on the head and body, the development of vertebral crests, the shape, scalation and coloration of the throat fan and neck lappets, and the coloration of the upper and lower patagium. However, with good binoculars and some patience and luck one may be able to identify several of the common species.

Spotted Gliding Lizard *Draco maculatus*
SVL to 8cm, total to 22cm

Henrik Bringsøe

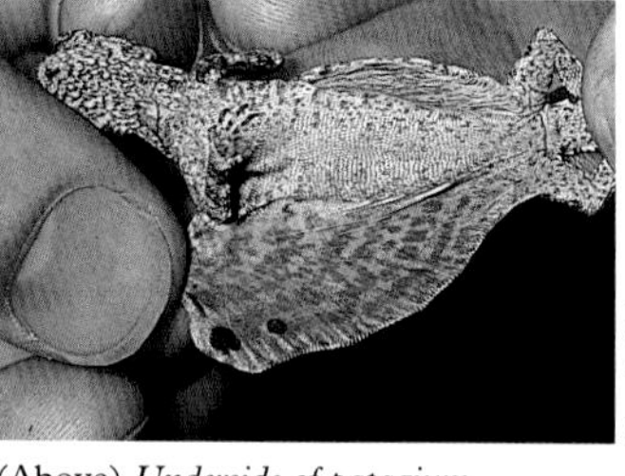

Henrik Bringsøe

(Above) *Underside of patagium*

This small gliding lizard is characterized by a yellow, orange or pink upper patagium with black spots, the presence of neck and tail crests, and small scales covering the tympanum. The coloration is variable, but usually the lower patagium is yellowish with several distal black spots, and the elongate throat fan shows a blue spot at its tapered base and yellow at the broad tip. Contrasting with other gliding lizards, this species inhabits seasonally dry, open, deciduous forest and monsoon evergreen forest from foothills to 1,400m altitude. It feeds mainly on ants, occasionally taking other small insects. Clutches contain 4 or 5 eggs. It inhabits much of mainland Southeast Asia, from Myanmar to Hainan to Penang.

Black-bearded Gliding Lizard *Draco melanopogon*

SVL to 8.5cm, total to 24cm

One of the smallest gliding lizards, and one of the most abundant. The male can be identified instantly by his long, black throat-fan, while both sexes have a black upper patagium with small yellow spots. It is most often seen on tree trunks at eye level, but also inhabits the canopy. It feeds predominantly on small and medium-sized ants and termites, and the odd small beetle or moth. Females usually lay 2 eggs. It inhabits closed shady rainforests in lowlands and at moderate elevations, to at least 800m altitude, from Thailand south of the Isthmus of Kra throughout Malaysia and Singapore to Sumatra, Borneo and the Natuna Islands.

Common Gliding Lizard *Draco volans*

SVL to 9cm, total to 22cm

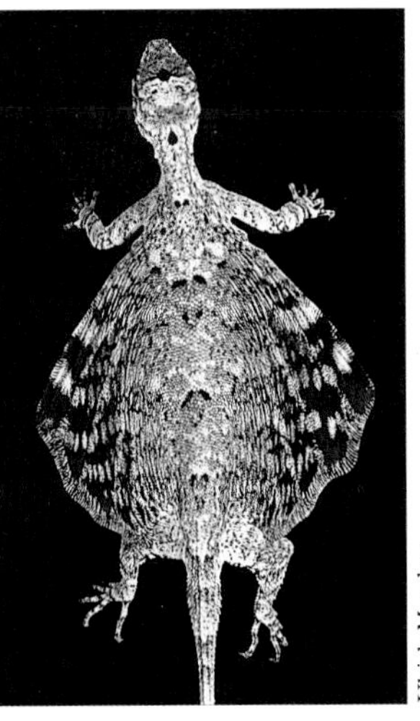

Ulrich Manthey

Males of mainland Southeast Asian populations have a rather short, triangular, yellow dewlap covered with small scales, and several differentiated nuchal crest scales, but no caudal crest. Six ribs support the patagium. The upper wing is brownish with dark blotches arranged in bands; the lower wing is soft blue with irregular black spots generally arranged in transverse series. There is extensive variation in coloration, scale characters and size within and among populations of this widely ranging species. This species is rather uncommon in rainforest, but it is often abundant in cultivated lands and near human habitation. Females lay 3 to 6 eggs. It occurs in Peninsular Thailand from Nakhon Si Thammarat south through Malaysia and Singapore to most of Indonesia and the Philippines.

Blanford's Gliding Lizard *Draco blanfordii*
SVL to 13cm, total to 38cm

Gernot Vogel

Peter Mudde

The coloration of the upper patagium differs between males and females of this large gliding lizard: in the male it is uniform olive-grey with fine longitudinal light lines or with darker olive mottling and a few red or maroon flecks on the outer posterior area; in the female there are transverse dark bands. In both sexes the lower wing is unmarked yellow. The elongate white dewlap of the male widens at the round tip; under the lappets is red to salmon. The presence of five ribs to support the patagium, obliquely directed nostrils, and a low caudal crest in the male, confirms the identity. It inhabits evergreen forest, and lays up to 4 oval eggs, measuring 14 × 7mm. It occurs from southwestern Yunnan through northern and western Thailand to northern Peninsular Malaysia.

(Top) *Female;*
(bottom) *patagium of male*

Dusky Gliding Lizard *Draco obscurus*
SVL to 10cm, total to 29cm

Wolfgang Wüster

Ulrich Manthey

This gliding lizard can be identified by the enlarged scales on the throat fan and neck lappets, and by the tympanum, which is at most only partially covered by small scales. The patagium is olive-grey above with a dark red outer edge, and dark blotches that often form four or five bands; the underside is uniform yellowish. The male has a raised ridge over the neck, a low tail crest of strongly keeled scales, and a rounded throat fan that is grey with a white edge, and has at its base a deep red blotch that extends to below the neck lappets. This species is moderately common on tall trees near forest edges and clearings in lowlands and hills. It feeds almost exclusively on ants and termites. Up to 5 eggs are laid in a clutch. This species occurs from southern Thailand to Sumatra and Borneo.

Five-banded Gliding Lizard *Draco quinquefasciatus*
SVL to 11cm, total to 27cm

Ulrich Manthey

This distinctive gliding lizard is instantly recognized by the pattern of the upper patagium: sharply defined black and orange bands continue across the back, with a series of white spots in the centre of each black band. Six ribs support the patagium. The tympanum is covered by small scales. The male's yellow dewlap is long and narrow, tapers to a fine point and is covered with small scales. This is a rather abundant species of tall evergreen lowland rainforest, particularly of peat swamp forest. It forages relatively low on tree trunks for ants, some termites and rarely other small insects. Females lay up to 4 eggs per clutch. This species ranges from Trang in southern Thailand through Malaysia to Sumatra and Borneo.

Barred Gliding Lizard *Draco taeniopterus*
SVL to 8cm, total to 23cm

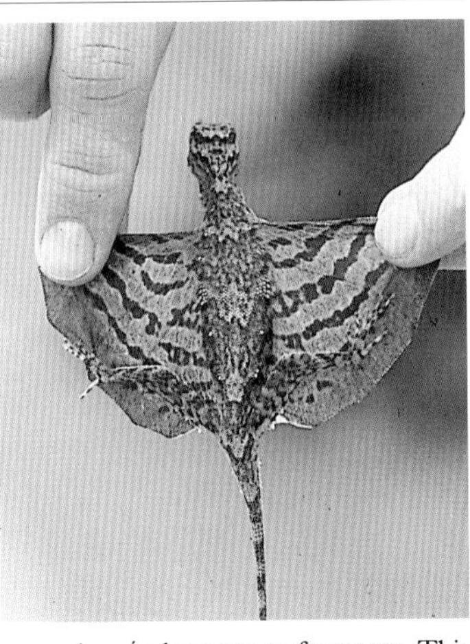
Ulrich Manthey

The patagium of both sexes is olive-yellow above with five broad, broken, black bands and a broad maroon outer edge; the lower surface is yellowish with the dorsal markings showing through. Five ribs support the wing. The male has a moderate-sized dewlap covered with large scales, which are red at the tapered base and pale green or olive at the broad tip. Under the lappets is red. The male lacks significant neck or tail crests. The female of this uncommon species produces up to four eggs. This species inhabits mountain and coastal regions from northern Thailand along the Thai-Myanmar border to southeastern and southern Thailand and likely Cambodia, but it is apparently absent from Peninsular Malaysia.

Indo-Chinese Water Dragon *Physignathus cocincinus*
SVL to 25cm, total to 90cm

This impressive lizard is mostly green, often showing several oblique pale-blue flank stripes, while the compressed tail bears dark bands. The male has swollen cheeks and crests of enlarged scales over the neck, back and tail. The female is somewhat smaller and lacks the crests. This beautiful agamid inhabits evergreen forest. It never strays far from water and is usually seen on tree branches overhanging streams. It feeds mainly on insects. Females bury 8–12 eggs in an exposed sandy patch in a stream bed; these hatch after nine or ten weeks. This species is at home in the south-eastern region and Khao Yai National Park in Thailand as well as in Cambodia, Vietnam and southern China.

BUTTERFLY AND SPINY-TAILED LIZARDS
(Family Uromasticidae)

The butterfly lizards were traditionally considered to belong to a single species that was included in the agamid family. Research in the past decades indicates that at least five species of butterfly lizards exist, and that they, together with the *Uromastyx* spiny-tailed lizards of Africa and the Indian region, are better assigned their own family. All butterfly lizards are inhabitants of arid habitats, where they dig deep burrows as refuges from heat, fire and predators. These spectacular lizards derive their common name from the boldly contrasting flank colours that are displayed to ward off intruders to their territories, and that, with some imagination, resemble a butterfly's wing when seen from above.

Pratheep Rojanadilok

Common Butterfly Lizards emerging from burrow

Common Butterfly Lizard *Leiolepis belliana*
SVL to 16.5cm, total to 49cm

Male in breeding splendour

The Common Butterfly Lizard is characterized by the small dorsal spots, not connecting to form a network or longitudinal lines, and the large, bold, orange and black marks along the entire flank. This fascinating lizard emerges from its burrow to bask in the morning sunshine, forage, and impress the neighbouring lizards during the day, and then retreats to its burrow in the late afternoon, closing the entrance with a plug of sand. It feeds mainly on plants, browsing buds and young shoots, but also eats beetle larvae, butterflies and other insects. The female lays 3–8 eggs in her burrow during the dry, hot period; striped juveniles with a reddish tail show themselves after the first heavy rains. The young share their mother's burrow for several months before digging their own burrows nearby. This beautiful species occurs throughout Thailand except the northeast, and in Tenasserim, Peninsular Malaysia, Sumatra and possibly Singapore.

Eastern Butterfly Lizard *Leiolepis reevesii*
SVL to 15cm, total to 50cm

Wolfgang Wüster

This species is similar to the Common Butterfly Lizard, but it differs in that its dorsal spots are much larger so that their dark edges form a continuous network. There are distinct longitudinal lines before the insert of the hind legs, while the contrasting flank pattern is less extensive. This species occurs in arid plateau habitats, where it establishes a home range of up to 30m square. Two mating seasons occur in a year in northeastern Thailand, from January to March and from May to August. This species occurs throughout the Mekong basin of northeastern Thailand, Laos, Cambodia and Vietnam, as well as southern China.

MONITOR LIZARDS (Family Varanidae)

The monitor lizards are typically large lizards of 'classical' proportions. They have a slender, deeply forked tongue, which is used to taste the air. Powerful, agile, swift if necessary and intelligent by lizard standards, monitor lizards are formidable hunters that have considerable ecological importance. About two-thirds of the 30-odd known monitor species inhabit Australia; only a few occur in Africa and Asia. Most feed on animal prey and occasionally carrion, but some eat fruits and vegetable food.

Bengal, or **Clouded, Monitor** *Varanus bengalensis*
SVL to 75cm, total to 175cm

Adult

Juvenile

This monitor is characterized by its brown base colour with numerous small yellow spots. The nostrils are situated about midway between the eye and the tip of the narrow snout. The neck scales are not greatly enlarged. This extremely adaptable species occurs in a wide range of habitats, from scrub desert to rainforest, yet it is most closely associated with dry, open forests. It is active during the day; at night it shelters in cavities, such as hollow trees, or in burrows dug in soil banks. Food consists mostly of beetles and other insects, which it finds by digging in leaf litter, rotting logs and cattle droppings, but larger prey makes a valuable contribution to the diet. Sexual maturity is reached after about three years. Females usually lay a single clutch of about 20 eggs early in the rainy season; hatchlings emerge several months later. This monitor occurs from Pakistan to Java and throughout our region.

Water Monitor *Varanus salvator*
SVL to 104cm, total to 260cm, exceptionally 321cm

This monitor, one of the largest lizards in the world, is recognized by the long, flattened snout which bears oval nostrils close to the tip. Its colour varies from blue-grey with a regular pattern of cream spots to uniform dull grey. It inhabits well-watered areas from coastal zones up to 1,200m, from mangroves and beaches to inland swamps, agricultural lands and montane forests. Active mainly during the day, it forages at the water's edge, in shallow water and in and among vegetation. Crabs and frogs are its preferred food, but its diet also includes eggs, nestling birds, small mammals, lizards, large invertebrates and carrion. Juveniles feed on insects. Clutches of 15–30 pliable elliptical eggs are laid early in the rainy season. The Water Monitor occurs from Sri Lanka through Southeast Asia to the Moluccas.

Harlequin Monitor *Varanus dumerilii*
SVL to 50cm, total to 125cm

Juvenile

Ulrich Manthey

The head of the juvenile Harlequin Monitor is bold orange, giving rise to its common name. Although this brilliant head coloration disappears with growth, the banded pattern on the neck and body persists into adulthood. The oblique, slit-like nostrils, located close before the eyes, are characteristic for this species. It inhabits dense evergreen rainforests and mangrove forests, particularly on islands, where it lives both on the forest floor and up in the trees. The Harlequin Monitor occurs in Tenasserim and the Mergui Archipelago, peninsular Thailand, Malaysia, Sumatra, and Borneo; there are no recent reports from Singapore.

The rare ROUGH-NECKED MONITOR (*Varanus rudicollis*) is similar; it is characterized by its greatly enlarged, strongly keeled neck scales that are arranged in 10–12 longitudinal series. It is dark with yellow crossbands and reddish areas on the side of the neck. Reaching 44cm in body length and 120cm in total, this arboreal monitor inhabits southern West Malaysia, Sumatra and Borneo.

GLASS LIZARDS (Family Anguidae)

Several of the genera in this family of relatively large lizards have no limbs and are easily mistaken for snakes. In contrast to snakes, however, they have functional eyelids and a distinct ear opening. Other genera, all in the New World, have well-developed limbs. All species have very heavy body armour in the form of bony plates under the scales, making them rigid to the touch. An expandable groove on the lower flank permits breathing. This family reaches its greatest diversity and abundance in central America. Two genera occur in Europe, one of these also inhabits Asia, where its species are restricted to temperate and montane tropical areas. The tail of Asian species is easily shed and regenerated.

Asian Glass Lizard *Ophisaurus gracilis*
SVL to 35cm, total to 54cm

Adults of this beautiful snake-like lizard are rich reddish-brown with blue crossbars. Juveniles are fairly drab pale brown above with small black spots; they also have one very dark brown band that runs from the snout, along the flank above the groove, to the tail and a second, much narrower band below the groove. The shiny rectangular scales form continuous longitudinal keels and are arranged in straight transverse rows. In Thailand, this species is a relic from a colder past, when the Chinese fauna ranged much further south. As the climate warmed, populations of the Asian Glass Lizard retreated northwards and higher onto mountain slopes. At present, it is known to inhabit two mountains in northern and northeastern Thailand at altitudes above 1,400m in areas of submontane forest with open rhododendron vegetation and short dense grass and herbs covering the ground. Here this lizard inhabits the undergrowth and is rarely seen except when basking on cool mornings or after rain. Its food consists mainly of insects. Between 4 and 7 eggs are laid among forest litter in the late rainy season; the eggs are guarded by the female. Hatchlings measure about 18cm. This interesting lizard occurs in the Himalayan foothills of northern India and southern China, northern Myanmar and northern Indo-China.

OLD-WORLD LIZARDS (Family Lacertidae)

Lizards of this family are typically relatively small, slender animals with a distinct head, a moderate body, well-developed limbs and a long tail. The latter character is taken to the extreme by the only species inhabiting tropical Southeast Asia. All lacertids have large head shields, small, granular dorsal scales and large ventral scales, and they bear femoral pores under the thigh. They typically live on the ground, on rocks or among undergrowth where they hunt small invertebrates during the day. Nearly all species lay eggs. The tail is easily shed and regenerated in case of predator attack. About 200 lacertid species inhabit Africa, Europe and Asia, but they are not particularly abundant or diverse in the oriental region.

Long-tailed Lizard *Takydromus sexlineatus*

SVL to 6.5cm, total to 36cm

Peter Mudde

This amazing little lizard has a tail almost six times as long as its head–body length. An exception to the family characteristic, the *Takydromus* species have longitudinal rows of large keeled scales on the back, and only the flanks bear fine granular scales. The ventral and tail scales are large and strongly keeled. This is a species of grassy areas, superbly camouflaged in its shape, texture and colour pattern to merge with dry grass. The long tail prevents it from falling as it climbs deliberately or moves rapidly through stands of tall tangled, interconnected grass or loosely matted grass and fine bamboo. It is active mostly in sunny weather and ranges from sea level up to 1,500m altitude. It deposits 2 or 3 eggs on the ground, usually at the base of a clump of grass or other vegetation. This species occurs throughout Southeast Asia and beyond, from Assam to Hong Kong and Sumatra, Java and Borneo.

SKINKS (Family Scincidae)

Skinks are by far the most diverse family of lizards: it contains almost 1,300 species comprising about one-third of all known lizard species. They are easily recognized by their modest size, their generally smooth, supple bodies with small legs or no legs at all, the large scales covering the head, and the rather uniform, rounded, overlapping scales on the body, limbs and tail, which may be smooth or keeled. Most skinks are terrestrial, many live among leaf litter or loose soil, and some have adapted to a completely underground lifestyle and have reduced or lost their limbs in the process, while a few have taken the opposite direction and become arboreal. Many skinks are diurnal but some, particularly the leaf litter dwellers, venture out in the open at dusk. Various species reproduce by eggs, others are live-bearing.

Many-lined Sun Skink *Mabuya multifasciata*
SVL to 13cm, total to 35cm

A large, heavy-bodied skink that usually has five or seven dark lines on the bronze back. The dark flank bears black-edged white spots, or a large orange patch in some individuals. It is heavier-bodied than the Long-tailed Sun Skink, and the tail is less than twice as long as the body. Relatively common near human habitation, river banks and large streams in lowlands and at moderate altitude, it is active during the day in sunshine, basking or foraging in clearings and on rocks, tree trunks, fences and coarse walls. It feeds on various substantial invertebrates. Females give birth to 5–10 young. The species is widely distributed from eastern India to Hainan and New Guinea.

Long-tailed Sun Skink *Mabuya longicaudata*
SVL to 11.5cm, total to 42cm

(Above) *Adult;* (below) *juvenile*

This graceful species is similar to one of the colour phases of the Many-lined Sun Skink, but the Long-tailed Sun Skink is proportionally more slender, and the undamaged tail is more than twice the length of the head and body. The body scales each bear two or three poorly developed keels. Juveniles are brass above and solid dark brown along the flanks. While this species co-exists with *M. multifasciata* over much of its range and habitat, it ranges into higher altitudes and further north, to Hong Kong and Taiwan, while it is absent from the Indian region and Indonesia. It appears somewhat more arboreal in its habits and lays eggs, 4–10 per clutch.

Rough-scaled Skink *Mabuya rugifera*
SVL to 6.5cm, total to 18cm

Ulrich Manthey

This attractive little skink has body scales that each bear five or seven very strong keels. Related to the large size of the body scales, there are only 24–28 scale rows around mid-body. The body may be uniform olive-green above or may bear five or seven yellowish longitudinal lines or series of spots. The undersurface is greenish-white. This uncommon skink inhabits little-disturbed rainforest from lowlands to above 1,200m altitude, and apparently favours areas near water. This species occurs in extreme southern Thailand, Peninsular Malaysia, Singapore, Sumatra, Borneo, Java, and the Nicobar islands.

Speckled Forest Skink *Mabuya macularia*

SVL to 6.5cm, total to 16cm

Juvenile

This active skink is characterized by its moderate size, a broad, somewhat flattened body, and keeled scales. Juveniles are steely blue-grey with a bronze head and white neck lines; mature adults are brown with speckled flanks and orange throat. Many animals have a rough ankle patch where parasitic red mites congregate among the scales, while some have a pocket behind the armpit where mites gather as well. The reason why a lizard would provide specialized residence areas to its parasites remains unclear, but it is thought that by concentrating the physical and biochemical discomfort caused by the mites in specific areas of its skin, the lizard can more effectively limit the mites' impact. This wide-ranging species shows considerable variation within and among populations in coloration, scale characters and mite patches; consequently, several subspecies have been described but are not universally recognized. While it is probably the most abundant reptile species in open deciduous forest, it is scarce or hard to see in evergreen forest. This terrestrial species forages among sparse undergrowth, basks on fallen branches, and preys on insects, spiders, and other small prey. The female lays 3 or 4 eggs underground in April; juveniles appear during the rainy season. It ranges from India throughout mainland Southeast Asia to northern Peninsular Malaysia.

Olive Tree Skink *Dasia olivacea* SVL to 11cm, total to 27cm

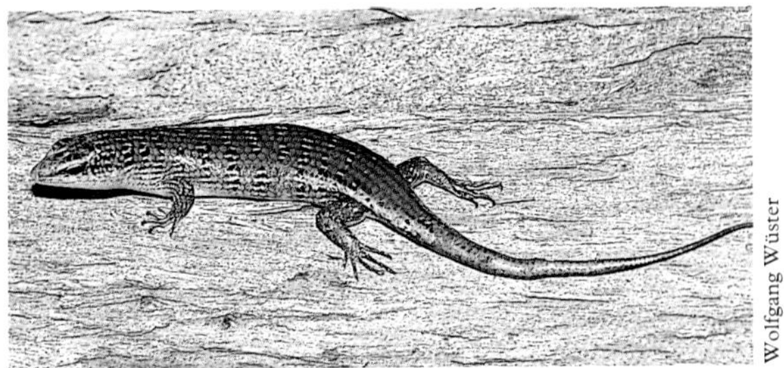

Wolfgang Wüster

The *Dasia* skinks resemble the large *Mabuya* species in their body proportions and keeled scales, but differ in the arrangement of the bones of the palate, their more pointed snouts and their exclusively arboreal habits. The Olive Tree Skink is identified by the smooth or weakly keeled dorsal scales, the six to ten vague dark bars or rings on the body and the additional rings on the neck and tail. In juveniles the black bands cover nearly the entire body, leaving only narrow yellowish lines and a uniform yellow or orange tail. This species prefers small islands and coastal forest, but also occurs in other forest types. It spends most of its time in the canopy, where it moves very deliberately. A female can lay several clutches of up to 14 eggs per year. This skink inhabits southern Thailand, Malaysia, Singapore, Borneo and Java.

Mangrove Skink *Emoia atrocostata*
SVL to 10cm, total to 26cm

Wolfgang Denzer

The various *Emoia* species are widely distributed throughout Indonesia, the Philippines and the Pacific islands, but only *E. atrocostata* has a tenuous foothold on the Asian mainland, occurring on the west coast of Peninsular Malaysia, on Penang and in Singapore. The *Emoia* species are small to moderate skinks that have a moveable lower eyelid with a clear window; they possess supranasal scales and the frontoparietal scales are fused. The Mangrove Skink is a moderately slender species with long legs. It usually has a black flank band, which may be so fragmented that it is barely distinct among the body spots. The scales are smooth. This skink inhabits mangroves and other coastal vegetation. A clutch invariably contains 2 eggs. It ranges from Malaysia to Taiwan, northeastern Australia and Vanuatu.

Bowring's Supple Skink *Lygosoma bowringii* (*Riopa bowringii*) SVL to 5cm, total to 11cm

This skink is typical of the *Lygosoma*, or *Riopa*, species and certainly the most abundant. In all species the limbs are short and cannot touch unless the body is flexed, small supranasal scales are present, and the tympanum is deeply sunk below the external ear opening. Bowring's Supple Skink has smooth or faintly keeled scales, a scaled lower eyelid, and a distinctive dark flank band with white spots, red behind the arm and yellow below. It lives in and among soft soil and leaf litter in forests, dry stream beds, gardens and other habitats from coastal areas up to 1,500m. It lays clutches of 2–4 eggs. This lovely little skink occurs in most of Southeast Asia.

Even-toed Supple Skink *Lygosoma isodactyla* (*Riopa isodactyla*) SVL to 8cm, total to 15cm

Jarujin Nabhitabhata

A very slender skink. The supranasals are not in median contact and fused to the nasals anteriorly, while the frontoparietals are fused together. The back, upper flanks and tail are dark olive, each scale with a dark edge and sometimes clouded with dark brown. The crown is black with some lighter spots. The species has been found in stone quarries, under small logs in open fields, and beneath stacks of firewood in a railway yard when steam trains were still in use. Its movements are active and snake-like, apparently not using the limbs when moving fast. This skink occurs in central Thailand between Nakhon Sawan and Ayutthaya and in Cambodia.

Khorat Supple Skink *Lygosoma khoratense* (*Riopa khoratense*) SVL to 11cm, total to 20cm

Gernot Vogel

A strongly elongate skink with small, widely separated pentadactyl limbs. The short thick tail suddenly tapers at the tip. The ear opening is very small. The supranasals are in mid-line contact and fused to the nasals anteriorly; the frontoparietals are paired. Snout scales are somewhat thickened. The dorsum is brownish, each scale with a dark brown edge and a vague dark spot at its base; the flanks are lighter, the venter pale grey, and the subcaudals darker. This burrowing skink inhabits low, limestone hills where it has been found under flat rocks or dug out of debris. It is restricted to the Dong Phaya Fai mountains between central and northeastern Thailand.

Short-limbed Supple Skink *Lygosoma quadrupes* SVL to 7cm, total to 15cm

Wolfgang Wüster

This very elongate skink represents the most derived state in the trend towards a burrowing lifestyle among the *Lygosoma* skinks. The limbs are much reduced but still have five digits. There is but a single frontoparietal, and supranasals are absent, presumably because they have fused with the nasal scale. The lower eyelid is covered by small scales. This species is usually found in decaying logs and is presumed to be a somewhat specialized predator on termites and their larvae. It produces 2 or sometimes 3 eggs per clutch, which hatch after about five weeks. This odd little skink inhabits most of Southeast Asia.

Striped Tree Skink *Lipinia vittigera*
SVL to 4.5cm, total to 10cm

A delicate little skink, immediately recognized by the bold black and cream lines on the head and body and the flame-orange tail. Fully arboreal, this species is a confident climber, moving with ease on tree trunks, buttresses and large logs. It occurs from lowlands up to a considerable altitude and inhabits closed tall forest, usually not far from streams or other sources of humidity. Its diet is unknown. The female lays 2–4 eggs, which are proportionally very large. Juveniles first appear during the monsoon rains. These shy animals are rarely seen, despite their wide distribution in most of tropical mainland Southeast Asia.

Speckled Leaf-litter Skink *Scincella reevesii*
SVL to 6cm, total to 16cm

The taxonomy of the *Scincella* group of skinks remains disputed: in Asia 12–32 species may be recognized, differentiated by scale counts, body proportions and subtle variations in coloration. All are generally greyish with a vague or distinct dark lateral band or spots. *Scincella* species are differentiated from some similar *Lygosoma* skinks by possessing nuchal scales, large eyes, greatly enlarged preanals and the absence of supranasals. This inconspicuous skink lives hidden among fallen leaves and other forest floor debris, hunting insects and other small invertebrates. This microhabitat makes the species extremely vulnerable to increasingly frequent forest fires. It inhabits seasonal evergreen forests from southern China to southern Thailand.

Spotted Forest Skink *Sphenomorphus scotophilus*
SVL to 7cm, total to 16cm

Ulrich Manthey

The dorsolateral dark line of this rare skink is broken into a series of dark brown spots, separated by buff spots, each dark spot usually divided below. The lips and sides of the neck are spotted black. There are 30–34 scale rows around the body. The median two rows of dorsal scales are widened somewhat, and all dorsals are wider than the scales on the flank. Nuchals are absent. It shows the defining characters of the genus *Sphenomorphus*: leg long enough to touch the hand, tympanum sunk, lower eyelid scaly, supranasals absent, frontoparietal paired, preanals distinctly enlarged. This species inhabits far southern Thailand, Peninsular Malaysia, Pulau Tioman and Sumatra.

Starry Forest Skink *Sphenomorphus stellatus*
SVL to 8cm, total to 18cm

Jarujin Nabhitabhata

This rarely seen lizard bears a median and two lateral series of more or less contiguous black spots, interspersed with small star-like light spots. The ground colour is greenish to bronze-brown above; the tail is lighter while the undersurfaces are greenish-white. Black spots are scattered over the head scales. The prefrontals fail to contact, and two or three pairs of oblique nuchals are present. The median dorsal row is the largest of the 22–24 smooth scale rows around mid-body. This attractive skink has been found under dead bark on a standing tree at moderate altitude. It occurs from Peninsular Malaysia and northeastern and southeastern Thailand to southern Vietnam.

Streamside Skink *Sphenomorphus maculatus*

SVL over 6cm, total to 16cm

Two individuals showing colour variations within a population

This lively little skink is slender but not elongated, the limbs are well developed, and the tail is almost twice the body length. A dark flank stripe, increasingly spotted with age, is characteristic, as are the concave rostral scale, the transparent lower eyelid, and 38–42 mid-body scale rows. The back may be nearly uniform bronze, but more often shows fine black spots arranged in longitudinal series. The undersurfaces are normally creamy white but during the breeding season, near the end of the rains, the venter becomes yellow while the underside of the tail becomes orange. Diurnal and terrestrial, it is commonly seen near streams in forested hill areas, foraging on rocks, sandy gravel or leaf litter. Its diet includes crickets, spiders, moths and other small invertebrates. The female lays a clutch of 4 or 5 eggs. This species occurs from eastern India and southern China through most of mainland Southeast Asia but apparently does not reach Peninsular Malaysia.

Indian Forest Skink *Sphenomorphus indicus*
SVL to 10cm, total to 28cm

Jarujin Nabhitabhata

Superficially similar to the Streamside Skink, this species differs in its convex rostral scale, the slightly larger, smooth body scales in 30–38 rows around mid-body, and the distinct dark stripe along the side of the head and flank. The black flank stripe may be unbroken as is typical of the species, or broken by vertical white lines characteristic of the subspecies *zebraicus*. This skink is occasionally found among leaf litter in monsoon evergreen forest at moderate and higher altitudes. Live-bearing, it produces 6–9 neonates per litter. It occurs in the Eastern Himalayan region, southern China and mainland Southeast Asia, possibly to Peninsular Malaysia.

Blotched Forest Skink *Sphenomorphus praesignis*
SVL to 11cm, total to 25cm

Ulrich Manthey

This species is distinctively variegated olive-green and brownish, with several large black blotches at the side of the neck and on the chest. There are 28 smooth scales around mid-body, the median two series of dorsals are enlarged, and the prefrontals are paired and in contact; three pairs of oblique nuchals are present and the median subcaudals are a little wider than adjoining scales. This species is known to occur among forest litter and decaying tree roots in montane evergreen rainforest with dense undergrowth between 800m and 1,280m. A litter of 6 has been reported. This rare species occurs in southern Thailand and Peninsular Malaysia.

Berdmore's Water Skink *Tropidophorus berdmorei*
SVL to 8.5cm, total to 19cm

Male

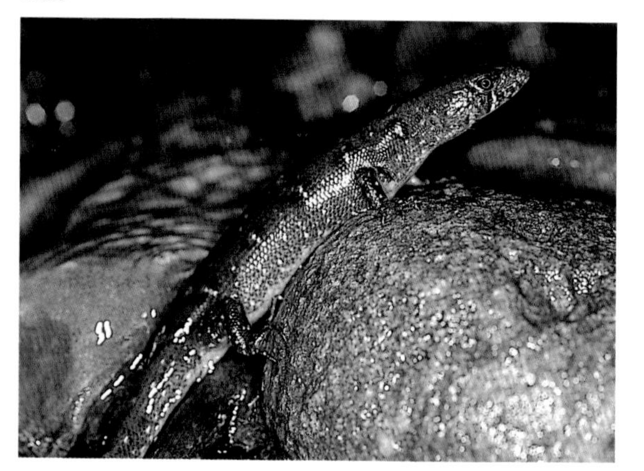

Female

The skinks of the genus *Tropidophorus* are immediately recognized by their tympanum, which is exposed at the body surface rather than deeply sunk behind the ear-opening, the enlarged preanal scales, the scaly lower eyelid, and the absence of supranasals. Most species, but not all, have keeled body scales. Berdmore's Water Skink has distinctly keeled scales when young, but these become smoother with growth. This species is further characterized by smooth upper head shields, smooth or obtusely keeled dorsal scales, and an undivided frontonasal scale. Ventrally it is salmon-pink. It favours small, rocky, forest streams at moderate altitudes, where it forages for water insects, small crustaceans and worms along the banks and under rocks in the stream bed. Ovoviviparous, females carry up to a dozen fertilized eggs within their bodies until the embryos are fully developed; the neonates emerge immediately from the eggshell after the egg is laid. This unusual lizard occurs from Tenasserim through northern Thailand and Laos to northern Vietnam and southern China.

Small-scaled Water Skink *Tropidophorus microlepis*
SVL to 8cm, total to 19cm

Jarujin Nabhitabhata

The strongly keeled flank scales arranged obliquely are diagnostic of this species, as are the sharply keeled dorsals that continue to four sharp ridges on the tail, the three preanal shields, and the rugose or striated upper head shields. The undersurface of the body is cream, the scales narrowly edged with dark brown. This skink inhabits small streams in evergreen forest at moderate altitude. Females produce litters of 7–9 young, which measure 56–60mm in total length. The Small-scaled Water Skink occurs in southeastern Thailand and on the Langbian plateau of Vietnam.

Northern Thai Water Skink *Tropidophorus thai*
SVL to 8cm, total to 16cm

Wolfgang Wüster

Similar to other water skinks in coloration, closer inspection reveals that this species' limbs are proportionally much smaller and can barely touch. The sharply keeled dorsal scales, rugose or striated upper head shields, divided frontonasal and frontal scales, and two enlarged preanal shields, together identify the species. Its pink ventral scales have light-brown edges, the blackish subcaudals bear irregular yellow marks. This species prefers evergreen forest at altitudes above 900m. It is the only regional *Tropidophorus* species that forages under leaves and logs on dry ground well away from streams and other permanent water sources. It is restricted in its distribution to a few mountain peaks in northern Thailand.

CROCODILES
(Order Crocodylia)

The 23 living species of crocodiles inhabit tropical and subtropical regions throughout the world. All species live in and near water, all are carnivorous and all lay eggs.

Sunda Gharial *Tomistoma schlegelii* TL to 470cm

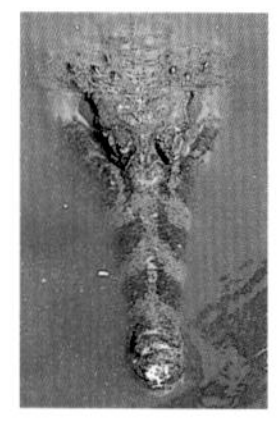

The long slender snout of this species is well-suited to capture fish and other relatively small prey with a quick sideways snap. It inhabits freshwater rivers, swamps and lakes. Females make a mound nest of vegetation debris on high ground near water, in which they lay 16–60 eggs. These hatch after 2½–3 months, at the height of the rainy season. This highly endangered species is native to southern Thailand, Malaysia, Sumatra and Borneo.

Saltwater, or **Indo-Pacific, Crocodile**
Crocodylus porosus TL to 700cm

The largest crocodile species, it is characterized by its long snout with lachrymal ridges from the eyes pointing towards the nostrils and the absence of enlarged neck scales immediately behind the head. It inhabits various coastal habitats, rivers and large lakes. Juveniles feed on insects, crabs, frogs and fish, taking ever larger prey, including large mammals, as the animal grows. With their fierce nature, animals must be considered **highly dangerous**. Females build a mound nest of rotting vegetation in which they lay up to 80 eggs and which they guard afterwards. This species occurs from India throughout Southeast Asia to Australia and the Pacific.

Siamese Crocodile *Crocodylus siamensis* TL to 400cm

This crocodile grows proportionally very broad and heavy with maturity, developing a wide head which, in old animals, has distinct bony ridges at the back of the skull. The bony lachrymal ridges form a broad-based triangle. Four large scales are present behind the head. This relatively good-natured crocodile feeds on moderately sized prey such as fish, frogs, birds and small mammals; unprovoked attacks on humans are unknown. Females lay 20–40 eggs. The Siamese Crocodile used to occur in most large lowland rivers in the region but was virtually extirpated from the wild in Thailand by the leather trade and to provide breeding stock for farms; populations in Vietnam and Cambodia remain poorly known.

Hybrid Crocodile *Crocodylus porosus* × *C. siamensis* TL over 600cm

In the 1950s, crocodile farming developed in Thailand in response to declining crocodile populations in the wild. Both the Siamese and Saltwater crocodiles were farmed. In the mid-1960s the two species were intentionally cross-bred, resulting in fertile offspring with characters of both parental species: a moderately broad snout, the lachrymal ridges meeting in the middle of the snout, and usually four moderate-sized scales present behind the head; the hybrids inherited the fierce temperament, fast growth rate and large size of the Saltwater parent. The hybrids tolerate captive conditions well, and their leather is of superior quality to either parent. Consequently, nearly all crocodile farms in the region breed this form.

TURTLES, TORTOISES AND TERRAPINS (Order Testudines)

These animals with their variety of English names form a very distinctive group of reptiles. The body is enclosed in the bony shell. Most species can withdraw their head, limbs and short tail inside the shell for protection from predators and drought. Many species have greatly modified these basic characteristics in their adaptation to environments as diverse as scrub-deserts, lowland swamps and open ocean, as exemplified by the long flippers of marine turtles or the reduced, flexible shell of soft-shelled turtles. Tortoises, terrapins and turtles generally take a long time to reach maturity, when their regular reproduction over a long life-span compensates for the high mortality of eggs and juveniles. Unfortunately, this survival strategy offers little resistance to the impact of human predators who succeed in breaking through the defensive armour of reproducing adults with steel tools or fire. Combined with the effects of habitat alteration, the result is that populations of most or all species in the region have been reduced and several species are seriously endangered.

BIG-HEADED TURTLES (Family Platysternidae)

This family contains just a single living species, which is restricted to temperate eastern and southeastern Asia, but fossil material is known from the Oligocene of Kazakhstan. Their affinity to other turtles is still debated: a relationship to tortoises and Batagurid hard-shelled turtles can be defended, as can a relationship to the chelydrid snapping turtles of North America.

Big-headed Turtle *Platysternon megacephalum* CL to 17cm

The massive triangular head, which is too large to be retracted into the flattened shell, the reduced plastron, the long tail, and the hooked upper jaw, are all characteristic of this bizarre turtle. Juveniles have a bright-brown carapace and head, orange plastron with black central blotch, brown and orange limbs and tail, and a cream stripe along the head and neck. With age this darkens: adults are often uniform dark brown. This fascinating animal inhabits small streams cascading down steep, rocky mountainsides where it hides under overhanging rocks during the day. The diet in the wild is unknown, but it is presumed to include snails, shrimps and frogs. It lays 2 or 3 elliptical eggs some distance away from the water. The species occurs uncommonly and localized in northern Thailand, Myanmar and Laos above 700m altitude, and at lower elevations in northern Vietnam and southern China.

ASIAN FRESHWATER POND TURTLES/ TERRAPINS (Family Bataguridae)

Mangrove Terrapin *Batagur baska* CL to 56cm

The smooth shell of this terrapin is perfectly adapted for swimming in the currents of mangrove-lined tidal estuaries. The broad, webbed front feet bear four claws (five claws in other species). Normally grey, both sexes turn black during the breeding season. The male remains smaller than the female and has a massive tail. This terrapin feeds predominantly on mangrove fruits. Females migrate to sandbanks, either upriver or along the coast, and over six weeks lay two or three clutches of about 20 eggs each. Populations of this highly endangered turtle survive in Peninsular Malaysia, Sumatra and the Sundarbans but continue to decline despite conservation efforts.

Red-headed Terrapin *Callagur borneoensis* CL to 60cm

Very similar to the Mangrove Terrapin but with five claws on the front feet. During the breeding season males develop brilliant-white heads with a black-edged red forehead and black lips, while the pale olive-grey shell shows black longitudinal lines and marginal spots. At other times they resemble females – grey-brown with a vaguely orange forehead. Females become substantially larger than males. They inhabit estuarine mangrove areas and feed on fruits, leaves and clams. Females migrate to upriver sandbanks or marine beaches to lay one to three clutches of 15–25 eggs. The round, brown hatchlings emerge about three months later. This threatened terrapin inhabits extreme southwest Thailand, Peninsular Malaysia and Borneo.

Yellow-headed Temple Turtle

Hieremys annandalii CL to 50cm

(Above) *Adult male;* (left) *hatchling*

Juveniles have a broad, round carapace with a sharp vertebral keel, distinct yellow stripes on the black head and neck, and a yellow plastron. As they grow the shell becomes elongated, raised and flattened above without a trace of the keel, the head becomes grey-brown with dense yellow speckling, and the plastron is smudged with black. This gentle species inhabits lowland swamps and feeds on aquatic plants. Males become larger and have a concave plastron. Females lay 4–6 large oblong eggs in a clutch. This uncommon species inhabits Thailand and the lower Mekong area.

Asian Giant Terrapin *Heosemys grandis* CL to 48cm

This large turtle always has a distinct, pale-brown keel over the dark carapace; each scute on the plastron has a radiating pattern and the head always has dense orange speckling. This species prefers lowland swamps and other damp areas but also occurs near seasonal streams in forested hills. It is equally at home in water and on land. Its diverse diet includes figs and other fruits, green vegetation and earthworms. Males have a concave plastron and become larger than females. Females in mainland Thailand lay 3–6, large, hard-shelled eggs in the dry season, which hatch several months later, early in the rainy season. This terrapin inhabits much of mainland Southeast Asia.

Spiny Turtle *Heosemys spinosa* CL to 23cm

Adult

Juvenile

In the bizarre juveniles of this species, each marginal scute is drawn out into a long sharp spike. There are also small spines on each costal scute and the vertebral keel is almost square in cross-section. With growth these spikes become indistinct. The radiated pattern of the plastral scutes, the absence of a distinct plastral hinge, the square keel on the five vertebral scutes, and the reddish neck, characterize adults. This turtle lives near streams in rainforest-covered hills. It spends much time hidden among forest litter, emerging occasionally early in the morning to feed on fruit and other vegetable matter. Several times per year 1 or 2 eggs are laid; these are enormous in proportion to the female. This rare species inhabits southern Thailand, Peninsular Malaysia, Sumatra, Borneo, the Natuna Islands and Mindanao.

Stream Terrapin *Cyclemys dentata* CL to 22cm

(Left) *Juvenile;* (above) *old female*

This small species has plastral scutes with a radiating pattern, orange-brown lines on the head and neck which fade with age, and a plastral hinge that develops with growth. It is the most common turtle of streams in forested hill areas at altitudes between 300m and 1,200m. Active at dawn and dusk, it feeds on fruits, leafy vegetation, invertebrates and carrion. It lays 1–3 large, hard-shelled eggs per clutch. Hatchlings measure about 55mm, are almost round and are more brightly coloured than the adult. It occurs in hill areas from Assam to Java and the Philippines.

Broad-backed Terrapin *Notochelys platynota* CL to 36cm

Hatchling

Wolfgang Grossmann

The presence of more than the normal number of scutes on the carapace is a common individual variation in most turtle species. In this species, however, the presence of an extra, sixth vertebral scute is a fixed characteristic. The broad carapace is flattened above and bears strong spikes along the posterior margin. Juveniles have a bright-greenish carapace with small black spots; this darkens to reddish-brown at maturity. The plastron is not, or only slightly, movable in adults; it is orange-red at all ages, with dark pigmentation increasing near the bridges with growth. This rainforest species feeds mainly on fruit. It inhabits southern Thailand, Malaysia, Sumatra and Java.

Asian Box Turtle *Cuora amboinensis kamaroma* CL to 21cm

The plastron of this attractive turtle has a complete hinge at all ages. This permits the two halves of the plastron to be independently raised, fitting tightly in the openings of the domed carapace and effectively closing up the whole shell. The graceful head bears fine yellow stripes. This is mainly a lowland swamp species, but individuals occur sporadically in forest and other places well away from water. They feed on fruits, soft vegetation, earthworms and other small prey. Males have a concave plastron and remain smaller than females. A clutch comprises 2–4 elongate eggs. Three subspecies occur from northeastern India to the Philippines and Moluccas; the subspecies *C. a. kamaroma* inhabits the mainland.

Rice-field Terrapin *Malayemys subtrijuga* CL to 21cm

This attractive little species is instantly recognized by the three strong carapace keels and the large head with its white stripes. The yellow plastron bears black blotches on each scute. Females grow much larger than males. This lowland species inhabits densely vegetated, shallow, warm, freshwater bodies. A specialized feeder, males eat only aquatic snails and occasionally small shrimp, while large females will also take small mussels. Up to 10 eggs are laid during the dry season, which hatch after the first heavy rain. This turtle is rather abundant in Thailand and southern Indo-China but is rare in Java and apparently absent from the intervening area.

Malayan Giant Terrapin *Orlitia borneensis* CL to 76cm

Wolfgang Grossmann

This rare turtle is typified by the massive head, the mushroom-shaped vertebral scutes, and the absence of greatly enlarged scales on the limbs. Juveniles have rather high shells but with growth the shell becomes proportionally flattened. The enormous adult size rivals the Alligator Snapper Turtle of the southern USA for the title of the world's largest freshwater hard-shelled turtle. It is blackish above and pale yellowish below; juveniles may have a dark rim under the marginal scutes. It is thoroughly aquatic in its habits. Despite its large size, very little is known about the biology or conservation situation of this species. It inhabits Peninsular Malaysia, Sumatra and Borneo.

Black, or **Smiling, Terrapin**

Siebenrockiella crassicollis CL to 20cm

Rarely seen, this small terrapin species is nevertheless one of the more abundant species in the region. The shape of the anterior vertebral scutes resembles a mushroom and the front legs bear some enlarged scales. This species is black except for the round white spots on the head and some brownish streaks on the plastral scutes. The short jaws, curved in a permanent smile, have the power to crush molluscs and scavenge carrion. Slow in its movements, and a poor swimmer, this species prefers shallow, densely vegetated, quiet water bodies in lowlands. It occurs in most of Thailand, Peninsular Malaysia, Sumatra, Borneo and Java.

Red-eared Terrapin *Trachemys scripta elegans* CL to 28cm

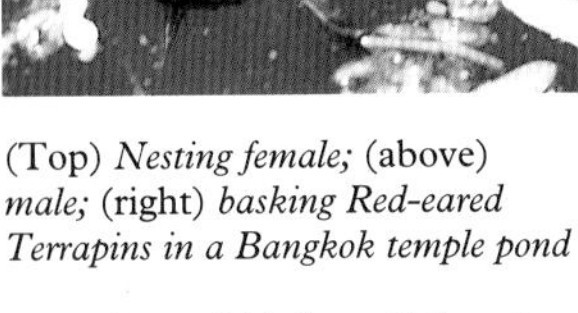

(Top) *Nesting female;* (above) *male;* (right) *basking Red-eared Terrapins in a Bangkok temple pond*

Hatchlings of this beautiful turtle are bright green with a pattern of yellow stripes and bars on the head, legs and carapace; the plastron is deep yellow with a round black spot on each scute. The side of the head bears an orange to blood-red elongated mark. As they grow, the animals become darker, particularly the carapace, but the red blotch and fine yellow stripes remain recognizable on the head and limbs. Males remain smaller than females, have less domed shells, and they have greatly elongated nails on the front feet, which they use to stroke the female's face during courtship. It is ironic that this exotic turtle species is by far the most conspicuous turtle in Southeast Asia. While the native turtle species spend the day submerged and hidden among vegetation, Red-eared Terrapins climb onto rocks, banks and other dry surfaces at the water's edge and spend their time basking in the full sunshine. The attractive hatchlings, imported from hatcheries in their native southern USA, are widely sold as pet animals. Quick to bite at anything resembling food, these pets are soon released into city parks, temple ponds and national parks. They feed on almost anything edible and grow rapidly. Although males appear to be relatively scarce, reproduction is successful under Asian tropical conditions. Consequently, while feral populations are concentrated in and around major cities at present, it is to be expected that this adaptable species will eventually spread through much of the region.

Elongated, or **Yellow, Tortoise**
Indotestudo elongata CL to 36cm

Juvenile

This attractive forest tortoise is the only species in the area with a greatly enlarged supracaudal scute above the tail. The rounded shell of juveniles grows more in length than in width, and adults are distinctly elongated. The animals are yellow with black blotches of variable size and density; individuals range from pure yellow to predominantly black. Males become slightly larger than females and develop a deep plastral concavity. This tortoise prefers deciduous forests, where it browses on shoots, buds, fruits and mushrooms. Females lay 2–4 eggs late in the rainy season, which hatch early in the next rainy season. This species ranges from northern India to Vietnam and to Perak in Peninsula Malaysia.

Impressed Tortoise *Manouria impressa* CL to 30cm

The beautiful Impressed Tortoise is quite variable in coloration, the shell ranging from uniform dark brown to flamed brown, black, yellow and orange, while the head can be orange-yellow or dark grey. All individuals, however, have a single large spur on the buttock. Males have a larger tail but otherwise resemble females. This rare tortoise species is restricted to hill and montane evergreen forest at considerable altitude. It spends much time resting under cover, emerging during rain to feed. Its diet consists mainly of forest mushrooms. About a dozen eggs are laid per clutch. This species occurs in isolated mountain populations in northern and western Thailand, Peninsular Malaysia and Indo-China.

Brown Asian Giant Tortoise *Manouria emys emys* CL to 50cm

This large tortoise has odd, reduced pectoral scutes on its plastron, which are widely isolated from each other. Each buttock bears a cluster of enlarged spiny scales. The shell and soft parts are dark brown-grey, sometimes with vague yellow clouds in the centre of each carapace scute. Males are nearly identical to females. Juveniles are proportionally less domed, and the vertebral and costal scutes may be somewhat concave. This form inhabits evergreen rainforest, preferring well-drained areas where it feeds on a variety of vegetation, fruits, mushrooms and, occasionally, animal matter. Clutches of about 30 eggs are known. It is found in southern Thailand, Malaysia, Sumatra and Borneo.

Plastron

Black Asian Giant Tortoise
Manouria emys phayrei CL to 58cm

This northern subspecies differs from the typical form in the shape of its pectoral scutes, which are in contact on the plastral mid-line. The uniform dark-grey to black carapace and plastron, and the larger maximum size, also typify this subspecies. It inhabits evergreen forests and is consequently restricted to hill areas, but apparently it does not ascend into the altitude region inhabited by the Impressed Tortoise. It feeds on a variety of vegetation, including bamboo shoots and banana trunks. Females can lay up to 51 eggs in a nest made of forest litter scraped together to form a mound. It inhabits northern, western and northern peninsular Thailand, and its range extends to northeastern India.

SOFT-SHELLED TURTLES (Family Trionychidae)

The soft-shells are characterized by flattened, partly flexible shells with reduced bony elements and tough skin instead of horny scutes. The head has a tube-nose, the extremely powerful jaws are hidden by soft lips, the neck is very long, and the widened front limbs bear only three claws. Most have a vicious temperament when disturbed; they can reach surprisingly far with their long necks and their sharp powerful jaws can inflict serious damage. Do not handle these animals unless you know how to do so safely.

Southeast Asian Soft-shelled Turtle

Amyda cartilaginea (*Trionyx cartilagineus*) CL to 83cm

While the soft-shelled turtles form an unmistakable group, identification of species is difficult. A long series of rounded tubercles along the anterior margin of the carapace characterizes this species. The variable coloration ranges from rich brown to purplish-black with black and yellow spots of varying intensity and pattern. The underside is nearly uniform white or pale grey. This purely aquatic species inhabits most types of fresh water. It feeds opportunistically on insect larvae, crabs, fish, fruits, seeds, and carrion. Females bury up to 30 eggs near the water's edge before the period of heaviest rain; hatchlings emerge some months later. This species is moderately common throughout Southeast Asia, except in the Philippines.

Hillstream Soft-shelled Turtle *Dogania subplana* CL to 26cm

This small soft-shelled turtle species has a proportionally large head. The sides of the carapace are almost straight, and the anterior margin of the carapace is completely smooth. The sides of the neck are usually tinted orange. The undersurface is white with black smudges at the margin. In Thailand and Malaysia this species inhabits swift-flowing streams with clear water and a rock or gravel bottom, but it has been reported from muddy pools in Java. Aquatic snails form an important part of its diet. Clutches contain 3–7 eggs. This relatively gentle-tempered species occurs in western and southern Thailand, Malaysia, Singapore, Brunei and Indonesia eastwards to Java.

Juvenile

Chinese Soft-shelled Turtle
Pelodiscus sinensis (*Trionyx sinensis*) CL to 25cm

Commercial culture of this aggressive little species has expanded enormously in recent years in tropical Asia. Its fast growth rate, early maturity and regular production of large clutches of eggs in tropical conditions make its culture more economical than native soft-shells. Juveniles are bright orange with black blotches below; with growth this fades to uniform cream. Mature adults are diagnosed by the single small tubercle at the anterior edge of the carapace. In its native area, this soft-shell inhabits a variety of lowland freshwater bodies. It feeds on small animals, particularly small mussels and fallen insects. Under tropical farming conditions, a female can produce up to six or seven clutches of 9–15 eggs. Hatchlings measure about 27mm; they grow fast and may mature in one year. This species is native to temperate eastern Asia but escaped or released animals can be found almost anywhere in Southeast Asia.

Striped Giant Soft-shelled Turtle *Chitra chitra* CL to 122cm

Jarujin Nabhitabhata

Kumthorn Thirakhupt

Juvenile

Superlative in its appearance, this boldly striped species is also one of the most endangered turtle species in the world. Long thought to represent a separated population of *Chitra indica* (of the Ganges and Indus systems), the arrangement of the lines on the neck and carapace and their persistence in old animals, as well as differences in scalation and the bony carapace, justify recognition as a separate species. It occurs in the Mae Klong river system of western Thailand, where the population has been reduced by hunting, consumption of eggs, collection for the animal trade and habitat impacts ranging from reservoir construction, sand dredging, riverbank erosion and water pollution. It feeds on fish and prawns. Females lay between 60 and 110 eggs, from which 45–50mm-long hatchlings emerge after about 65 days.

Asian Giant Soft-shelled Turtle or **Frog-headed Soft-shell** *Pelochelys cantorii* (formerly *P. bibroni*) CL to 120cm

Kumthorn Thirakhupt

The carapace, head, neck and limbs of this impressive soft-shell are olive-grey or brownish, either uniform or with small black specks and (rarely) some white spots. The eyes are close to the snout tip and the nose is short, but the head is much less elongated than in *Chitra*. This soft-shell prefers estuarine regions, but also occurs in coastal mudflat areas and large rivers far inland. It probably feeds on fish, prawns and crabs. This rare species occurs from southern India throughout Southeast Asia to southern China and New Guinea.

MARINE TURTLES
(Families Dermochelyidae and Cheloniidae)

The seven species of cheloniid marine turtle and the unique Leatherback Turtle are superbly adapted to the marine environment. Their shells are streamlined and the front limbs are elongated for efficient swimming; these characteristics are complemented by many other anatomical and physiological developments. All species, however, must return to land to lay their eggs. While sea turtles have survived ecological and environmental changes for millions of years, persistent human over-exploitation and habitat disturbance have reduced many populations to critical levels.

Leatherback Turtle *Dermochelys coriacea*
CL to 180cm or more

Wolfgang Wüster

Juvenile

The unique Leatherback Turtle has a skin-covered carapace which has seven ridges, which in juveniles are covered by white scales. An awesome and intriguing species, it is at home in the open waters of oceans and deep seas. They are exceptionally strong swimmers, crossing oceans against the current and making regular foraging migrations into temperate waters following jellyfish aggregations, returning in the autumn when the water cools. Counter-current heat-exchangers in their circulatory system and heat-generating tissues enable them to retain a body temperature several degrees warmer than the surrounding water. They are able to make regular deep dives, down to 970m. Leatherbacks feed almost exclusively on jellyfish, comb-jellies and salps. Nesting occurs at night on steep sandy beaches along deep open water. The female digs a nesting hole up to a metre deep and deposits between 50 and 140 spherical eggs (diameter about 55 mm) as well as up to 100 small, yolkless 'eggs'. Their function may be to prevent sand from falling among the larger eggs. After closing the nest, the female makes several circular crawls around the area, which hides the exact location of the nest. Female leatherbacks may nest up to nine times per season. The eggs hatch after 50–60 days; the hatchlings average 57mm in carapace length and 38g in weight. Their dispersal and natural growth rate remain a mystery. Leatherbacks nest on many tropical beaches; in Southeast Asia, nesting areas exist in Myanmar, the Andaman Sea coast, and at Trengganu on Peninsular Malaysia's northeast coast.

Green Turtle *Chelonia mydas* CL to 140cm

Hatchlings

The Green Turtle is easily recognized by the small, blunt head with a single pair of prefrontal scales and the four pairs of non-overlapping carapace scutes. The carapace is quite variable in coloration but the animal is always white below. Hatchlings have distinctive white edges along the flippers and the carapace. The Green Turtle feeds almost exclusively on sea grass and therefore inhabits shallow coastal areas with clear water and a sandy bottom. Females undertake epic migrations to nest on sandy beaches where they deposit one or more clutches of about 100 eggs over the course of a nesting season. The females return to their feeding grounds and usually do not nest again until some years later. The eggs hatch about two months after laying and after a night-time dash across the beach the hatchlings swim frantically offshore for two or three days, presumably to reach their juvenile feeding areas among floating seaweed. The Green Turtle used to occur abundantly in most tropical coastal waters, but collection of eggs, hunting of adults and other human influences have depleted or extirpated many populations.

Hawksbill Turtle *Eretmochelys imbricata* CL to 93cm

Roger S. Thorpe

(Above) Juvenile; (below) hatchling

The Hawksbill has four pairs of distinctly overlapping costal scutes, two pairs of prefrontal scales and long, pointed jaws. The shell is flamed brown with a cream underside, while hatchlings are blackish below. Hawksbills live on coral reefs, usually around offshore islands. They feed mainly on sponges but also take other organisms. Nesting beaches occur scattered throughout the tropics; while this prevents large-scale egg collection and slaughter of adults, it also complicates conservation efforts. Clutches contain 32–250 eggs. As demand for its carapace scutes, the so-called 'tortoise-shell', continues, populations decline further.

Olive Ridley Turtle *Lepidochelys olivacea* CL to 75cm

This relatively small sea turtle has many more carapace scutes than the standard five vertebrals and four pairs of costals. Adults are mainly olive to grey above and white below. Hatchlings are completely dark grey but the plastron brightens after several weeks. This species is believed to prefer sandy or muddy coastal waters. It feeds rather opportunistically on crabs, prawns, tunicates, jellyfish and other animals as well as algae. Females usually come ashore in aggregations to deposit between 80 and 160 eggs several times in a nesting season. Occurring in most tropical seas, this species originally foraged and nested along most coasts of Southeast Asia, but most populations have been seriously depleted and several are now near extinction. The LOGGERHEAD TURTLE (*Caretta caretta*) occasionally wanders into Thai coastal waters. This reddish-brown species always has five pairs of costal scutes; its carapace length may approach 120cm.

arboreal Living in trees or other vegetation.
aquatic Living in water.
carapace The dorsal shell of a turtle.
CL Carapace Length: the maximum length of the carapace of a turtle, including spines, measured in a straight line parallel to the plastron in the case of tortoises and freshwater turtles, and measured with a tape over the curve of the carapace in sea turtles.
compressed Flattened from side to side.
depressed Flattened from top to bottom.
distal Away from head or body.
diurnal Active in daylight.
dorsal The top or upper side of an animal, including the upper surfaces of the tail and limbs.
dorsum The back of an animal, restricted to the body only.
fossorial Living underground.
immaculate Not spotted.
Indo-China Laos, Cambodia and Vietnam.
keel A raised longitudinal ridge on an individual scale or on a turtle shell.
melanistic Completely black.
nocturnal Active at night.
oviparous Egg-laying.
ovoviviparous Reproduction by retaining the eggs to develop in the female's body, but not providing nourishment beyond the yolk; the female gives birth to fully developed juveniles.
patagium The wide fringe of skin supported by elongated ribs at the flank of *Draco* lizards; it can be expanded to act as a gliding sail.
pelagic Living in open water.
phylogenetic The inferred relationships of evolutionary descent of species and groups.

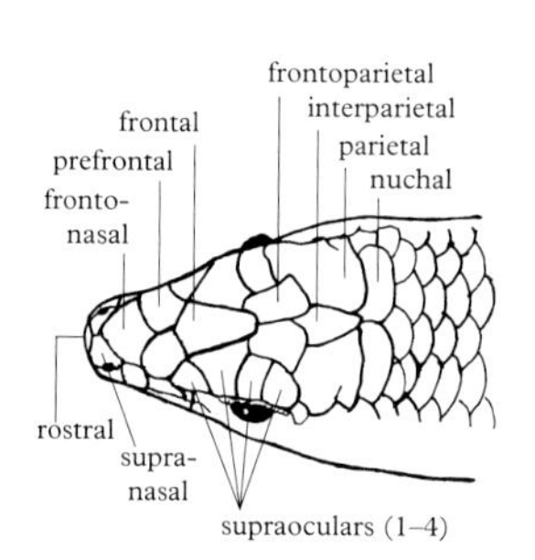

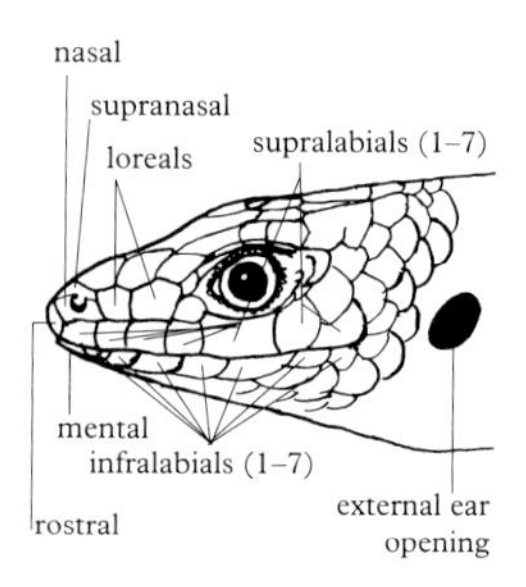

*Head scales (shields) of a Long-tailed Sun Skink (*Mabuya longicaudata*).*

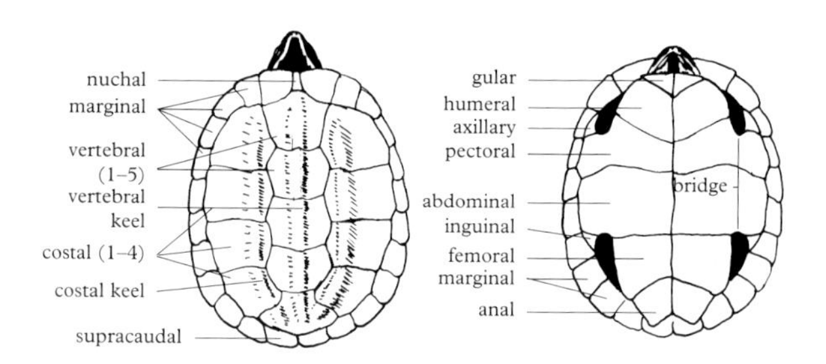

*Scutes of the shell of a Ricefield Terrapin (*Malayemys subtrijuga*).*

plastron (adj. plastral) The underside of a turtle's shell, covered by the gular, humeral, pectoral, abdominal, femoral, and anal scutes.

preanal The area before the vent or anus of lizards; special pores or enlarged scales may be located here.

preanofemoral In the area before the vent and continuing along the underside of the thigh.

proximal Near the head or body.

riparian Living along the margins of streams, rivers or lakes.

scale The keratinized elements covering the head, body, limbs and tail of lizards and snakes and sometimes the head and limbs of turtles. The larger ones on the head are often called shields.

scansor An expanded small plate (a lamella) under the finger or toe of a gecko, which provides grip on smooth surfaces. Also termed a subdigital lamella.

scute A large keratinized plate covering the shell of a turtle.

shield *see* **scale**

subcaudal scale (subcaudals) A scale on the underside of the tail.

subdigital lamella *See* Scansor.

SVL Snout–Vent Length: the distance from the tip of the snout to the end of the vent (or anus) of a snake, lizard or crocodile.

terrestrial Living on the ground, including among forest leaf litter.

TL Total Length: the length of head, neck, body and tail together.

venter The belly or underside of the body.

ventral The lower surfaces of an animal including the undersides of the tail and limbs.

vertebral Along or over the spine (the backbone).

viviparous Live-bearing; strictly speaking, vivipary involves the developing embryo obtaining additional nourishment from the female's uterus as well as from yolk.

Further reading

Cox, M. J. 1991. *The Snakes of Thailand and their Husbandry*. Krieger Publishing Co., Malabar, Florida. 526 pp.

David, P., and Vogel, G. 1996. *Snakes of Sumatra – An Annotated Checklist and Key with Natural History Notes*. Edition Chimaira, Frankfurt am Main, Germany. 260pp.

Lim, K. K. P. and Lim, F. L. K. 1992. *A Guide to the Amphibians and Reptiles of Singapore*. Singapore Science Centre, Singapore. 160 pp.

Manthey, U. and Grossmann, W. 1997. *Amphibien und Reptilien Südostasiens*. Natur- und Tier-Verlag, Münster, Germany. 512 pp.

Payne, J. M. and Cubitt, G. *Wild Malaysia*. New Holland (Publishers) Ltd, London.

Pritchard, P. C. H. 1979. *Encyclopedia of Turtles*. T.F.H. Publications, New Jersey. 895pp.

Ross, C. A. (ed.). 1989. *Crocodiles and Alligators*. Weldon Owen Pty. Ltd, Australia. 240 pp.

Smith, M. A. 1930. The Reptilia and Amphibia of the Malay Peninsula from the Isthmus of Kra to Singapore, including the adjacent Islands. *Bulletin of the Raffles Museum*, No. 3, pp. 1–138, Singapore.

Smith, M. A. *The Fauna of British India, Ceylon and Burma, Including the Whole of the Indo-Chinese Sub-region*. Vol. 1, *Loricata, Testudines*, 185pp, 1931; Vol. 2, *Sauria*, 440pp, 1935; Vol. 3, *Serpentes*, 583pp, 1943. Taylor & Francis Ltd, London.

Stewart-Cox, B., and Cubitt, G. 1995. *Wild Thailand*. New Holland (Publishers) Ltd, London. 208 pp.

Taylor, E. H. 1963. The Lizards of Thailand. *The University of Kansas Science Bulletin*, Vol. 44 (14), pp. 687–1077.

Taylor, E. H. 1965. The Serpents of Thailand and adjacent waters. *The University of Kansas Science Bulletin*, Vol. 45 (9), pp. 609–1096.

Zhao, E. and Adler, K. 1993. *Herpetology of China*. SSAR Contributions to Herpetology, Number 10. 522 pp.

Index